DIETETICS FOR HIGH SCHOOLS

THE MACMILLAN COMPANY
NEW YORK · BOSTON · CHICAGO · DALLAS
ATLANTA · SAN FRANCISCO

MACMILLAN & CO., Limited
LONDON · BOMBAY · CALCUTTA
MELBOURNE

THE MACMILLAN COMPANY
OF CANADA, Limited
TORONTO

DIETETICS FOR HIGH SCHOOLS

A TEXTBOOK IN NUTRITION AND FOOD ECONOMICS

REVISED EDITION

BY

FLORENCE WILLARD

CHAIRMAN OF THE DEPARTMENT OF HOME ECONOMICS,
WASHINGTON IRVING HIGH SCHOOL,
NEW YORK CITY, N.Y.

AND

LUCY H. GILLETT

SUPERINTENDENT OF THE NUTRITION BUREAU,
N.Y.A.I.C.P.,
NEW YORK CITY, N.Y.

NEW YORK
THE MACMILLAN COMPANY
1930

COPYRIGHT, 1920, 1930,
BY THE MACMILLAN COMPANY.

———

Set up and electrotyped.   Published July, 1920.
Reprinted January, September, 1925; July, 1926;
July 1927; October 1928.
Revised edition published August, 1930.

· PRINTED IN THE UNITED STATES OF AMERICA ·

PREFACE TO SECOND EDITION

Our newer knowledge of that phase of nutrition, which shows the relation of vitamins and mineral elements to growth and health, has brought about such important developments in our ideas about the family diet, during the last ten years, that a revision of this book has been considered necessary. As this knowledge concerning the relation of diet in early years to health in adult life increases, we are more and more impressed with the importance of acquiring good food and other health habits during the growing period.

Teachers have a wonderful opportunity to arouse in the youth of today an appreciation of this fact; they also have a partial responsibility in helping them to develop such habits as will increase the vigor and resistance of the men and women of the future.

The purpose of this book is to help teachers to present the principles of nutrition in a clear and simple, yet scientific, manner and to show the relation between these facts and other health habits so that they may the more easily be applied in a general health program. Problems are scattered throughout the text to help the student to see the personal application of these principles rather than to think of them as isolated facts.

The authors wish to acknowledge their indebtedness to Professor Henry C. Sherman for his valuable advice and helpful criticisms and suggestions in the prepara-

tion and revision of the manuscript; and to Doctor
M. P. Burtis for the work involved in the revision of
Tables XXII, XXIII, XXIV, XXV, and XXVI in
Chapter VI.

F. W.
L. H. G.

SUGGESTIONS TO TEACHERS

The home economics teacher holds a joint responsibility with the physical education teacher, the school doctor, the school nurse, and the science teacher for the health of the students in her school. Because she has made a special study of food and its effect upon growth and health, the nutrition phase of the health program is usually under her supervision. *Dietetics for High Schools* has been written to help her arouse in high-school girls and boys an appreciation of the advantages of forming correct food and other health habits.

The authors have tried to present the material in such a way that it will create in the student a voluntary interest in his own food needs and in the effect food has on growth, health, and activity, but they do not mean to imply that lesson plans will be unnecessary. A teacher may desire to change the manner of approach if the one here presented does not seem logical to her. We suggest that she review the subject matter carefully, study the methods of presentation, look up the references assigned for each chapter, and go into her classroom with her own plan of work, fortified by an enthusiasm which is necessary to stimulate students. If Mrs. Rose's "share method" of evaluating foods appeals to her as a more concrete and graphic way of presenting the subject, she will be able to adapt this new method to the material in this book by supplementing Chapter VII with *Foundations of Nutrition* by Rose.

The material as here presented may be used in the last year of junior high school or in any year in senior high school. The subject matter has been planned to cover one year of study with five recitation periods a week. Two double periods with one single period each week constitute the most satisfactory arrangement for time, but when this is impossible, the work as arranged may be adapted to single periods.

When time is so limited as to make it impossible to prepare food for demonstration purposes during the class period, meals may be illustrated by assembling food from the school lunch room, or food may be purchased outside the building, or brought from home. Many of the problems call for home work which may be utilized for supplying the food for the shorter-period work, but whatever the source, it is of the utmost importance that students work with the actual foods.

If the laboratory consists of unit kitchens with a connecting classroom for class work, members of the class may take turns in illustrating different parts of the problems. For instance, while one half of the class prepares the food for demonstration, the other half may discuss and check the calculations of the first half. The slow-moving group should handle the simpler problems; also, their time may be used to better advantage in visualizing amounts of foods and food combinations than in calculations. The group plan is especially practical where there is a student assistant.

In *Dietetics for High Schools*, the Irving family is used to illustrate specifically the food problems of a large family consisting of adults and children of various ages. A type family offers a common problem which makes for a better understanding, but students may find it more interesting to substitute their own families for the work.

If students appear specially interested in different phases of the subject, they may be encouraged to start worth-while projects along the lines of their particular interests. Many of the problems are simple projects, which may be changed to cover a wider field when the opportunity presents itself. The following are some of the projects that have been suggested by students, and completed with the help of the teacher: planning and providing the proper foods for an underweight or over-weight member of a family; working out the food budget for someone who has a limited income; assuming the teaching of health habits to a primary class; providing a program on health in a school assembly or at a meeting of the Parent-Teacher Association.

The questions at the end of each chapter are merely suggestive for oral review. Each teacher will doubtless plan her own objective questions to be used for mid-term and final examinations.

A note book should be kept by each student in which to record the weight chart, the health score card, the 100-Calorie portions of common foods, and the various problems involving data that will be used later when computing dietaries.

The laboratory should be equipped with an accurate scale and a measuring rod. Students should weigh and measure themselves the first week of each month and record results. We find that the interest in weight is a very satisfactory approach to the study of foods. Students seem to remember the measure of the 100-

Calorie portions of foods after they have weighed and measured them. Therefore we recommend dietetic scales for the weighing of foods, and advise that all common foods be weighed and measured to give the student a basis upon which to make later calculations. The laboratory should be equipped with portable tables, three and one half feet by two and one half feet; there should be one table to each four students, the tables to be used for the display of food materials and family meals. These will take the place of desks in the recitation end of the laboratory.

As supplementary reading to *Dietetics for High Schools*, we recommend:

BROWN, C. M. and HALEY, A. H. *Teaching Home Economics*. Houghton Mifflin Company (1928).

HARRIS, J. W. and LACEY, E. V. *Everyday Foods*. Houghton Mifflin Company (1927).

ROSE, MARY S. *Feeding the Family*. The Macmillan Company (1929).

ROSE, MARY S. *Foundations of Nutrition*. The Macmillan Company (1927).

ROSE, MARY S. *Laboratory Handbook for Dietetics*. The Macmillan Company (1929).

SHERMAN, H. C. *Chemistry of Food and Nutrition*. The Macmillan Company (1926).

WINCHELL, F. E. *Food Facts for Every Day*. J. B. Lippincott Company (1924).

CONTENTS

CHAPTER I

PAGE

OUR DEPENDENCE ON FOOD 1

Relation of food to growth, health, and activity. Average weight for height; a safety zone. Weight charts. Factors other than food that influence nutrition. A nutrition score card. Questions. References.

PROBLEMS

1. To find the weight and height of each member of the class.
2. To find the average age, weight, and height of the whole class.
3, 4. Weight charts.
5. To score health habits.

CHAPTER II

THE ENERGY VALUE OF FOODS 26

The dangers of chance selection of food. The Calorie, a measure of food value. 100-Calorie portions of foods. A comparison of the energy value of different foods. Questions. References.

PROBLEMS

6. To learn to use the scales.
7, 8, 9, 10. To find the measure of 100-Calorie portions of grain products (7), fruits (8), vegetables (9), and of dairy products and some fats (10).
11. To compare fuel value and cost of various foods.
12, 13, 14. To find the measure of the 100-Calorie portions of meat and fish (12), nuts (13), and of sweets (14).

CONTENTS

PROBLEMS   PAGE

15. To select a luncheon from the 100-Calorie portions.

16. To select an economical luncheon from the 100-Calorie portions.

CHAPTER III

ENERGY REQUIREMENTS OF INDIVIDUALS 43

Amount of energy needed may be expressed in Calories. Energy varies with size and activity and is influenced by growth and clothing. Questions. References.

PROBLEMS

17, 18, 19,   To find the food requirements of various
20, 21, 22.   types of people.

23. The food value of a box luncheon.

24. To plan a day's food for a girl.

25. Cost of meals calculated.

CHAPTER IV

THE COMPOSITION OF FOODS 61

Digestion and absorption. Interrelationships between the various foodstuffs in their functions in the body. Carbohydrates; kinds, sources, and uses. Fats; sources, uses, and amount required. Protein; occurrence, uses, kinds and their relative values, amount required. Amino acids. Questions. References.

PROBLEMS

26. To separate the cellulose and starch in potato.

27. To compare the fat content of various foods.

28. To plan an 800-Calorie meal using one ounce of fat.

29. To plan a meal in which one third of the energy is from cereals, breadstuffs, and potatoes.

30. To find the amount of energy in one pound of fudge.

31. To compare the economic value of various foods as sources of energy.

32, 33. To calculate the protein requirements of various people.

PROBLEMS   PAGE

34. To find the amounts of given foods which
    will be necessary to satisfy the protein
    requirements of various people.

35, 36. To select and arrange a combination of
    foods which will satisfy the protein re-
    quirement of a given group.

CHAPTER V

MINERAL ELEMENTS   88
    Mineral elements described. Importance of. The acid-
base influence of foods. Calcium; occurrence, uses, and
amount required. Phosphorus; occurrence, uses and a
safety allowance. Iron; occurrence, uses, and a safety
allowance. Iodine. Questions. References.

PROBLEMS

37. To find the amount of each of various foods
    which will supply one gram of calcium.

38. To find the amount of each of several foods
    necessary to supply one gram of phos-
    phorus.

39. Plan, for a high school girl, a day's meals
    containing a variety of foods that will
    furnish proper amounts of calcium, phos-
    phorus, and iron.

40. Prepare the meals planned in Problem 39.

41. Compare the mineral elements in the meals
    prepared in Problem 40 with the mineral
    elements in the diets of girls in the class.

42. To calculate the amount of calcium, phos-
    phorus, and iron needed by a family
    group.

43. Make lists of foods valuable for calcium,
    phosphorus, and iron.

CHAPTER VI

VITAMINS   107
    Vitamin A; importance of, safety allowance, sources,
effect of heat on. Vitamins B and G; importance of, a safety

allowance, sources. Effect of water on vitamins B and G. Vitamin C; importance of, sources, a safety allowance. Effect of heat, water, and alkali on vitamin C. Vitamin D; importance of, and sources. Vitamin E. Questions. References.

PROBLEMS

44. List the foods valuable for each vitamin.
45. Arrange exhibits of foods valuable for each vitamin.
46. To select foods to insure an adequate vitamin supply.

CHAPTER VII

FOOD SELECTION 129
Food needs summarized. Selection of foods according to (a) food groups; (b) Calories and grams of protein, calcium, phosphorus, and iron with proper attention to foods valuable for vitamins; (3) shares of each food factor. Questions. References.

PROBLEMS

47. To find food requirement in shares.
48. Shares of each food factor in meals arranged according to the 100-Calorie portions.
49. To make a graphic representation of foods according to shares.

CHAPTER VIII

FEEDING THE IRVING FAMILY 147
Luncheons for high school girls and boys. Growth is very rapid during the adolescent period. Food needs are unusually high. The meals should be very nourishing as well as attractive. The box luncheon. The school luncheon. The home luncheon. Questions. References.

PROBLEMS

50. To reconstruct meals previously planned.
51. To determine the number of shares in these meals.
52. To prepare a suitable noonday meal.

PROBLEMS   PAGE

53. To select a luncheon from the school menu.
54, 55, 56. To plan and prepare luncheons suitable for high school girls and boys.

CHAPTER IX

FOOD FOR THE BABY 165

Mother's milk, the best food. Cow's milk, the best substitute. Modified milk. Supplementary foods. Cleanliness of milk and utensils is very important. Regularity of feeding is essential. Questions. References.

PROBLEMS

57. To determine the food value of the food for a baby six months old.
58. To keep milk cold without a refrigerator.
59. To prepare the meals for a child one year old.
60. To calculate the energy and protein value of the meals prepared in Problem 59.
61. To calculate the cost of feeding a child one year old.

CHAPTER X

FOOD DURING THE SECOND YEAR 186

Milk, vegetables, fruit, and bread and cereals are very important. Diets for children during the second year. Questions. References.

PROBLEMS

62. To review the proper cooking of vegetables.
63. To prepare the fruit juice for a child two years of age.
64. To prepare a day's meals for a child 14 months of age; 24 months old.

CHAPTER XI

FOOD FOR CHILDREN FROM TWO TO FIVE YEARS OF AGE . . 197

Milk is still a very important food. Grain products, vegetables, and fruits in the diet. Value and use of eggs. Meat is not a necessity. Fats are valuable. Sweets should be used cautiously. Good food habits are essential. Questions. References.

PROGRAMS PAGE

65. To plan and to compare two breakfasts.
66. To become familiar with the grain products most useful for their mineral elements.
67. To make a chart showing the relative value of various grain products.
68. To review the cooking of cereals.
69. To become familiar with the vegetables furnishing mineral elements in largest amounts.
70. To prepare the day's meals for a child three years of age.
71. To prepare the day's meals for a child five years of age.
72. A discussion of common practices in the feeding of children.

CHAPTER XII

FOOD FOR SCHOOL CHILDREN AND ADULTS 219

The meals of a family may be planned to provide for the needs of both school children and adults. Both need milk, vegetables, grain products, fruit, and fats. Eggs may be eaten by all. Meat is not a necessity. Questions. References.

PROBLEMS

73. To plan and prepare, for a boy, a day's meals with a pint of milk concealed in cooked foods.
74. To plan and prepare, for a family, a day's meals with one pint of milk per person in cooked foods.
75. A comparison of the cost of milk and meat.
76. To plan, for a boy, a day's meals with one third of the energy supplied by grain products.
77. Suitable substitutes for inappropriate foods commonly given to children.
78. To plan the weekly supply of vegetables for a family.
79. To compare the cost of reasonable meat and milk supplies for a family.

PROBLEMS   PAGE

80. To plan a day's meals for a school girl and
    boy.
81. To plan and prepare a dinner for a family.
82. To plan a regulating diet.
83. To plan a reducing diet for a girl 15 years
    of age.
84. To plan a fattening diet for a girl 15 years
    of age.

CHAPTER XIII

PLANNING THE MEALS FOR A FAMILY 243

Foods may be so prepared that one meal may be appropriate for the whole family. Accurate calculation of a few
meals is valuable. A score card. Questions. References.

PROBLEMS

85. The preparation and comparison of the cost
    of two meals.
86. The planning of one-dish meals.
87. The planning, preparation, and serving of
    the meals for a family.
88. To judge the relative merits of two meals by
    means of a score card.

CHAPTER XIV

THE MARKETING ORDER AND METHOD OF BUYING 261

Planning ahead. Buying in large quantities. Standing
orders for staple foods. Good buying helps in economy.
A record of food purchased will help to regulate food expenditures. Questions. References.

PROBLEMS

89. To list foods that may be purchased in large
    quantities.
90. To make an estimate of the amount of each
    of the supplies listed in Problem 89 needed
    by a given family.
91. To study economy in meats.
92. A comparison of the cost of delicatessen
    store and home-cooked products.
93. A comparison of the price of prunes pur-
    chased under different conditions.

PROBLEMS   PAGE

94. A comparison of the use and cost of dried and fresh fruit.

95. The use and cost of dried milk and butter substitutes.

96. A comparison of the cost of cereals purchased in bulk and in packages.

97. To study the cost of "telephone service and delivery."

98. To plan the meals for a week for some member of the class.

99. To plan the market orders in Problem 98.

100. A study of the "balance of food values" in a given weekly food record.

101. To order the food for the family at home for a week.

LIST OF TABLES

CHAPTER I   PAGE

I. Average weights and heights for children under five years of age 9

II. Average weights and heights of girls over five years of age 10

IIA. Mean weight of short, medium, and tall girls . . 12

IIB. Range in height of short, medium, and tall girls . 12

IIC. Annual gain in mean weight of short, medium, and tall girls 13

III. Average weights and heights of boys over five years of age 14

IIIA. Mean weight of short, medium, and tall boys . . 16

IIIB. Range in height of short, medium, and tall boys . 16

IIIC. Annual gain in mean weight of short, medium, and tall boys 16

CHAPTER II

IV. Weight and measure of the 100-Calorie portions of common grain products 31

V. Weight and measure of the 100-Calorie portions of common fruits 32

VI. Weight and measure of the 100-Calorie portions of common vegetables 34

VII. Weight and measure of the 100-Calorie portions of various dairy products and some fats . . . 35

VIII. Weight and measure of the 100-Calorie portions of various kinds of meat and fish 37

IX. Weight and measure of the 100-Calorie portions of some common nuts 38

X. Weight and measure of the 100-Calorie portions of sweets and sugars 39

CHAPTER III

XI. Energy used by average-sized men per hour under different conditions of activity 48

LIST OF TABLES

PAGE

XII. Average Calorie Requirement per pound per hour
for adults 50
XIII. Food allowances for children 53
XIV. Calories for each pound of body weight during the
growing period 55
XV. Food requirements after middle age 56

CHAPTER IV

XVI. Grams of fat and carbohydrate in the 100-Calorie
portions of common foods 74
XVII. The relative value of common foods for protein . . 78
XVIIA. Foods grouped in the order of the amount of protein
in the 100-Calorie portions of common foods . . 79
XVIII. Grams of protein for growing children according to
Calorie need 84

CHAPTER V

XIX. Foods grouped according to the amount of calcium
in 100-Calorie portions of common foods . . . 97
XX. Foods grouped according to the amount of phosphorus in 100-Calorie portions of common foods . . 100
XXI. Foods grouped according to the amount of iron in
100-Calorie portions of common foods 103

CHAPTER VI

XXII. Food value of 100-Calorie portions of vegetables . 120
XXIII. Food value of 100-Calorie portions of fruits . . . 122
XXIV. Food value of 100-Calorie portions of grain products 123
XXV. Food value of 100-Calorie portions of fats and sugars 124
XXVI. Food value of 100-Calorie portions of meat, fish,
eggs, cheese, nuts 125

CHAPTER VII

XXVII. Share value of 100-Calorie portions of foods . . . 139

CHAPTER IX

XXVIII. Suggested formulae for modified milk 172
XXIX. Supplementary foods for babies 174
XXX. Calorie and protein value of the diet of a child one
year of age 178

CHAPTER X

XXXI. Meals for a child from fourteen to eighteen months
of age 193

PAGE

XXXII. Meals for a child from eighteen to twenty-four
months of age 194

CHAPTER XI
XXXIII. Meals for a child during the third year 200
XXXIV. Meals for a child during the fourth year 214
XXXV. Meals for a child during the fifth year 215

CHAPTER XIII
XXXVI. The food requirements of the Irving family in
Calories and grams 245
XXXVII. The food requirements of the Irving family in terms
of shares 246
XXXVIII. Mrs. Irving's meal plan 252
XXXIX. The food value of the meals given in Table XXXVIII 253
XL. The food value of the meals planned by Mrs. Irving
where calculations were not made 254

CHAPTER XIV
XLI. Leaks in Alice's grocery order 264

LIST OF CHARTS

CHAPTER I
                          PAGE

I. Increase per year in the weight of girls 4
II. Increase per year in the weight of boys 4
III. Increase per year in the height of girls 5
IV. Increase per year in the height of boys 5
V. Method for preparing the weight chart 18
VI. The safety zone for weight 20
VII. An actual weight record kept by a Washington
Irving High School girl 21

CHAPTER IV
VIII. Grams of carbohydrate per 100 Calories 69
IX. Grams of fat per 100 Calories 75
X. Grams of protein per 100 Calories 77
XI. Influence on growth of tryptophane and lysine . . 81

CHAPTER V
XII. Effect of an adequate salt mixture on growth . . 90
XIII. Effect of a suitable salt mixture on growth . . . 91
XIV. Grams of calcium per 100 Calories 96
XV. Grams of phosphorus per 100 Calories 99
XVI. Grams of iron per 100 Calories 102

CHAPTER VI
XVII. Growth curve of rats with vitamin A 109
XVIII. Variations in the rate of growth due to differences
in the amount of vitamin A 110
XIX. The result of too little vitamin C 115

CHAPTER VII
XX. One share of a man's daily requirement 135
XXI. One share of white potato 137
XXII. One share of white bread 138

CHAPTER XI
XXIII. Relative food value of milk, cocoa, and tea or coffee 202
XXIV. Relative food value of the 100-Calorie portions of
sugar, molasses, and fruit 212

CHAPTER XIV   PAGE
    XXV. Relative value of various foods as factors in the diet   272
   XXVI. Relative value of grain products and nuts   .   .   .   273
  XXVII. Relative value of various green vegetables   .   .   .   274
 XXVIII. Relative value of roots and tubers   274

LIST OF ILLUSTRATIONS

CHAPTER II   PAGE
   Diagram of a bomb calorimeter   27

CHAPTER III
   2. A respiration calorimeter   46

CHAPTER IV
   3. A representation of the digestive tract   64
   4. Influence of complete and incomplete proteins   . . .   82

CHAPTER V
   5. Influence of calcium on the growth of rats   94

CHAPTER VI
   6. Influence of vitamin D during the growing period   . . 119

CHAPTER VIII
   7. Baby Betty 146
   8. Good posture position   151

CHAPTER IX
   9. Influence of sunlight on the growth of chickens   . . . 183

DIETETICS FOR HIGH SCHOOLS

CHAPTER I

OUR DEPENDENCE ON FOOD

Good health is universally prized and desired. In any health scheme food plays a very important part. Other controlling factors are sleep, fresh air, sunshine, exercise, good posture, and the absence of physical defects. Correct weight for height and age is one sign of physical fitness.

Food for Growth, Health, and Energy

Every boy and girl dreams of a happy future. One of the greatest assets in the enjoyment of life and in the fulfillment of cherished plans is good health. Boys and girls who take advantage of every opportunity to become and to keep strong and healthy will be happier, find work easier, bring more comfort to those about them, and they will be of greater value in the welfare of their country. The ability to work, to accomplish one's aim, and to compete with those physically strong may depend upon the attention given to the laying of a good foundation for health in early years. For good health good nutrition is necessary; for good nutrition food must be selected to meet the needs of growth, health, and energy.

1

Food is the source of our energy. Every action, whether voluntary (as walking, swimming, sewing, or typewriting) or involuntary (as breathing and the digestion of food), must have some power back of it. This power or energy comes from the strength built into or stored in the muscles by the food eaten. And as the result of activity, whether visible or invisible, another form of energy is produced, which keeps the body warm. This energy is heat.

Growth is impossible without food. When we stop to think what has happened during the "growing-up" process, we realize that there is a wonderful difference between a small, dependent baby and a strong, active boy or girl. The bones are larger, muscles have developed, teeth have appeared, strength has increased, and many other changes have taken place. These changes have come gradually through growth or the building up of a body by means of food.

Constant repair work is necessary. Both voluntary work with the muscles and the everyday processes of living — such as heart beat, circulation of the blood, and the action of the digestive tract and other organs — cause a constant wearing away of tissue. This waste is carried out of the body by way of the skin, lungs, kidneys, and intestines, and it must be replaced daily for the rebuilding of the worn-out parts, or strength will fail. Food must provide for this repair work as well as for the formation of new growth material.

The rate of growth may be influenced by food. Scientists tell us that not only growth but the rate of growth of their experimental animals in the laboratories may be influenced, either favorably or unfavorably, by the kind and amount of food eaten. Animals that grow slowly and are undersized when certain food factors are missing in their diets will be stimulated to grow more rapidly and to attain normal size (if stunting has not continued over too long a time) when these missing substances are given them.

Health is affected by food. In the same way, animals may be made strong or weak; their teeth may be made to grow sound and straight or carious and crooked according to foods fed; they may be made to grow old at an early age and subject to certain diseases, or to retain their youthful characteristics, with freedom from disease, for a longer period through a regulation of certain food factors. All these and other differences which appear with variations in the diets of animals convince us that food may be equally effective in influencing the lives of men, women, and children.

This information makes a valuable tool. Do not these facts create a desire to study foods more closely and to learn about the power they possess whereby growth and health are stimulated and regulated? Such knowledge puts into the hands of boys and girls a tool which will be valuable in helping them to make of themselves what they will.

Periods of Most Rapid Growth

It is very important for children of all ages, and for adults, to have food adjusted to their varying needs, but Charts I, II, III, and IV show that it is especially desirable for children during the first year, and for boys and girls of high-school age, to eat plenty of food containing growth materials. These are the periods of most rapid growth.

During the first year of a child's life he gains from 12 to 14 pounds. During the second year of life he must eat enough to gain an average of 6 pounds, and in addition the food eaten must keep in repair the 12 or 14 pounds gained during the first year of life. Then dur-

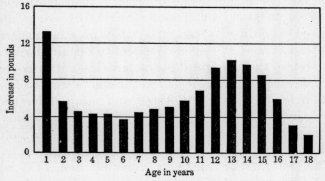

Chart I. — Increase per year in the weights of girls

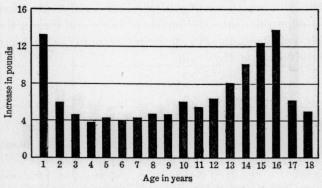

Chart II. — Increase per year in the weights of boys

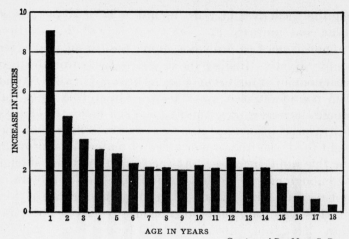

Courtesy of Dr. Mary S. Rose

Chart III. — Increase in height of girls from birth to the eighteenth year

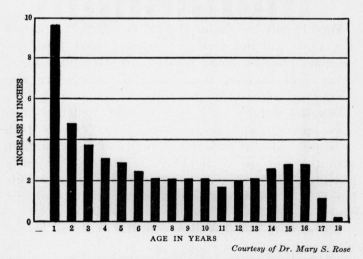

Courtesy of Dr. Mary S. Rose

Chart IV. — Increase in height of boys from birth to the eighteenth year

ing the third year he must maintain 25 or 26 pounds of bone and muscles, and must eat enough in addition to gain from 4 to 5 pounds more, and so on year after year. By the time a boy or girl is twelve or thirteen years old, or of high-school age, there are between 80 and 100 pounds to keep in repair. About this time the weight increases very rapidly, as is shown by the charts. Extra precautions are necessary in the selection of the right food with the proper kinds of materials to provide for this rapid increase. At the same time there should be enough energy so that the food needed for growth is not used in other ways. Many boys and girls are thin at this age, and more susceptible to disease, because they have not eaten sufficient food to provide for growth, energy, and resistance.

Factors Other than Food

Food is only one factor in good nutrition. A perfect diet alone will not produce health. Sleep, fresh air, sunshine, exercise, good posture, the free drinking of water, and freedom from physical defects are also controlling factors.

Physical defects. Physical defects — such as diseased and enlarged tonsils, adenoids, and carious teeth — secrete poisons into the system and thus interfere with the best use of food by the tissues. A yearly physical examination, with the correction of any defects found, will provide a body free to gain — the first health essential.

Sleep. Growth takes place and the wear and tear of work and play go on while a person sleeps. Too little sleep gives too little time for growth and repair. Long hours of restful sleep are necessary if the body is to make good use of the food eaten.

HOURS OF SLEEP REQUIRED

AGE	HOURS OF SLEEP OUT OF EACH 24 HOURS
Babies under six months	18 to 22
Babies from six months to one year	18 to 20
Children from one to two years	14 to 15
Children from two to five years	13 to 15
Children from five to eight years	11 to 12
Children from eight to twelve years	10 to 11
Boys and girls from twelve to sixteen years	9½ to 10
Those over sixteen years	8 to 9

Fresh air. Fresh air stimulates the appetite, helps the body to transform food into tissue, and enables us to work and play with less fatigue. Everyone should be out of doors for at least one to two hours each pleasant day and sleep with windows open at night. Fresh air both day and night is as necessary for growth and health as food.

Sunshine. Sunshine is as necessary for the optimum growth of strong, healthy boys and girls as it is for plants or animals. Illustration No. 8 shows the effect of sunshine on the growth of two chickens. These two chickens are of the same age; they had the same food and the same care, except that chicken A was in the sun for one half hour each day, while chicken B had no sunshine. Sunshine stimulates the body to build strong muscles, to make good red blood, and to develop a resistance to disease. Everyone needs direct sunlight for a part of each pleasant day.

Exercise. Exercise increases the appetite, aids digestion, and makes the blood circulate more freely, thereby helping to build better and stronger bodies. It encourages deep breathing, which strengthens the various internal organs and helps them to function normally. It tends to prevent constipation and other abnormal conditions; it also helps to give a clear complexion. Exercise is very important in growth and health, but it must be accompanied by the right food and plenty of sleep and rest.

Posture. Good posture not only improves one's personal appearance but it allows the internal organs to do their work properly. Poor posture cramps the lungs, stomach, liver, and other organs until they are unable to function as nature intended they should. Every boy and every girl should learn to sit, stand, and walk erect. Illustration No. 7 offers an inspiration for correct standing.

Water. Plenty of water in the diet keeps the tissues in a moist condition, stimulates the flow of digestive juices, aids in digestion, absorption, and excretion, and promotes circulation. We need plenty of water to flush the system so that we may get rid of the waste material before it becomes injurious. It is no longer considered unwise to drink a moderate amount of water with meals, provided it is not used to wash down the food. With an average amount of exercise, at least six to eight glasses of water should be taken every day. A convenient and easy rule to remember is to take one glass of water before breakfast, a glass or two with each meal, a glass about two hours after each meal, and a glass before going to bed. More may be taken with increased exercise and a corresponding increase in evaporation or perspiration.

WEIGHT IS ONE INDEX OF PHYSICAL FITNESS

How much do you weigh? One means of determining physical fitness is through weight. Weight should be average for height and age. During the period of high-school life, boys and girls gain, normally, from 9 to 10 pounds a year, or from 12 to 13 ounces a month. By referring to Tables II and III each student may find his average weight. There is no cause for alarm, however, if the weight of the individual does not correspond exactly with this figure.

TABLE I. — HEIGHTS AND WEIGHTS FOR CHILDREN UNDER FIVE YEARS OF AGE (Based on Data Published by the Children's Bureau, U. S. Department of Labor)

AGE	BOYS		GIRLS	
	Height	Weight	Height	Weight
	Inches	*Pounds*	*Inches*	*Pounds*
Birth	20.6	7.6	20.5	7.2
3 mos.	23.5	13.0	—	—
6 mos.	26.5	18.0	25.9	16.8
9 mos.	28.1	20.4	27.6	19.1
12 mos.	29.4	21.9	28.9	20.8
15 mos.	30.8	23.6	30.1	21.9
18 mos.	31.8	24.6	31.3	23.4
21 mos.	32.9	25.8	32.3	24.8
24 mos.	33.8	27.1	33.4	26.4
27 mos.	34.8	29.0	33.9	27.3
30 mos.	35.4	29.5	34.9	28.3
33 mos.	36.1	30.6	35.6	29.1
36 mos.	37.1	32.3	36.8	30.5
39 mos.	37.9	33.1	37.3	31.6
42 mos.	38.6	33.8	38.0	32.5
45 mos.	39.0	34.5	38.5	33.3
48 mos.	39.5	35.9	39.0	33.8
5 years	41.6	41.1	41.3	39.7

TABLE II. — HEIGHTS AND WEIGHTS FOR GIRLS OVER FIVE YEARS OF AGE [1]

Height,[2] Inches	Age, Years													Height, Inches
	6	7	8	9	10	11	12	13	14	15	16	17	18	
	Weight, Pounds													
37.5 — 38.4	33	33*	—	—	—	—	—	—	—	—	—	—	—	37.5 — 38.4
38.5 — 39.4	34	35*	—	—	—	—	—	—	—	—	—	—	—	38.5 — 39.4
39.5 — 40.4	36	36*	—	—	—	—	—	—	—	—	—	—	—	39.5 — 40.4
40.5 — 41.4	37*	37*	37*	—	—	—	—	—	—	—	—	—	—	40.5 — 41.4
41.5 — 42.4	39	39	39*	40*	—	—	—	—	—	—	—	—	—	41.5 — 42.4
42.5 — 43.4	41	41	41*	41*	—	—	—	—	—	—	—	—	—	42.5 — 43.4
43.5 — 44.4	42	42	42*	43*	44*	44*	44*	—	—	—	—	—	—	43.5 — 44.4
44.5 — 45.4	45	45	45	45*	46*	46*	46*	—	—	—	—	—	—	44.5 — 45.4
45.5 — 46.4	47	47	48	48*	48*	49*	49*	—	—	—	—	—	—	45.5 — 46.4
46.5 — 47.4	50	50	50	50	50*	51*	52*	—	—	—	—	—	—	46.5 — 47.4
47.5 — 48.4	52	52	52	52	53*	53*	54*	—	—	—	—	—	—	47.5 — 48.4
48.5 — 49.4	54	54	55	55	56	56*	58*	58*	58*	—	—	—	—	48.5 — 49.4
49.5 — 50.4	56*	56	57	58	59	61	62*	63*	64*	—	—	—	—	49.5 — 50.4
50.5 — 51.4	59*	59	60	61	61	63	65	66*	69*	—	—	—	—	50.5 — 51.4
51.5 — 52.4	62*	63*	64	64	64	65	67	69*	71*	—	—	—	—	51.5 — 52.4
52.5 — 53.4	65*	66*	67	67	68	68	69	71*	73*	—	—	—	—	52.5 — 53.4
53.5 — 54.4	—	69*	69	70	70	71	71	73*	75*	—	—	—	—	53.5 — 54.5
54.5 — 55.4	—	72*	72*	74	74	74	75	77	78*	79*	—	—	—	54.5 — 55.4
55.5 — 56.4	—	75*	76*	76	78	78	79	81	83*	86*	89*	—	—	55.5 — 56.4
56.5 — 57.4	—	—	79*	80*	82	82	82	84	88	92*	96*	100*	—	56.5 — 57.4

Height²																
57.5 — 58.4	—	—	—	—	—	—	84*	84	86	86	88	93	96*	101*	103*	—
58.5 — 59.4	—	—	—	—	—	—	87*	87	90	90	92	96	100	103*	104*	—
59.5 — 60.4	—	—	—	—	—	—	90*	91*	95	95	97	101	105	108	109	111*
60.5 — 61.4	—	—	—	—	—	—	—	96*	99	100	101	105	108	112	113	116
61.5 — 62.4	—	—	—	—	—	—	—	101*	104*	105	106	109	113	115	117	118
62.5 — 63.4	—	—	—	—	—	—	—	—	108*	110	110	112	116	117	119	120
63.5 — 64.4	—	—	—	—	—	—	—	—	112*	114*	115	117	119	120	122	123
64.5 — 65.4	—	—	—	—	—	—	—	—	116*	118*	120	121	122	123	125	126
65.5 — 66.4	—	—	—	—	—	—	—	—	—	122*	124	124	125	128	129	130
66.5 — 67.4	—	—	—	—	—	—	—	—	—	126*	128*	130	131	133	133	135
67.5 — 68.4	—	—	—	—	—	—	—	—	—	130*	131*	133	135	136	138	138
68.5 — 69.4	—	—	—	—	—	—	—	—	—	—	134*	135*	137*	138*	140*	142*
69.5 — 70.4	—	—	—	—	—	—	—	—	—	—	136*	136*	138*	140*	142*	144*
70.5 — 71.4	—	—	—	—	—	—	—	—	—	—	138*	138*	140*	142*	144*	145*

* The starred figures represent values based upon theoretical computations instead of on exact averages.

Age is taken at the nearest birthday; for example, a child is considered 6 years old from 5 years, 6 months to 6 years, 5 months, and 29 days, inclusive.

Weight is taken at the nearest pound.

In these standards a certain percentage of net weight has been included to allow for clothing, except shoes and sweaters, which are removed when weight is taken:

For weight from 35 to 63 pounds, 3 per cent of the net weight has been included.

For weight from 66 to 82 pounds, 2.5 per cent of the net weight has been included.

For weight 83 pounds or more, 2 per cent of the net weight has been included.

[1] Prepared by Bird T. Baldwin, Ph.D., Iowa Child Welfare Research Station, State University of Iowa, and Thomas D. Wood, M.D., Teachers College, Columbia University, New York City.

[2] In taking height, stand with heels together and heels, shoulders, and head against the wall. Avoid stretching above a normal height.

TABLE IIA. — MEAN WEIGHT OF SHORT, MEDIUM, AND TALL GIRLS

	AGE, YEARS												
	6	7	8	9	10	11	12	13	14	15	16	17	18
	WEIGHT, POUNDS												
Short . . .	39.5	44.1	48.6	52.8	57.8	63.4	69.3	80.9	92.7	101.9	110.1	110.4	111.7
Medium . .	45.0	50.9	56.8	63.0	69.0	76.4	85.6	99.6	108.9	115.5	119.4	121.4	121.6
Tall . . .	53.4	58.9	66.5	75.2	83.6	94.2	106.8	118.5	125.1	128.6	132.8	132.6	134.9

TABLE IIB. — RANGE OF HEIGHT OF SHORT, MEDIUM, AND TALL GIRLS

	AGE, YEARS												
	6	7	8	9	10	11	12	13	14	15	16	17	18
	HEIGHT, INCHES												
Short — Less than	43.5	45.5	47.5	49.0	50.5	52.5	54.5	57.5	59.5	60.5	61.5	61.5	61.5
Medium — { From	43.5	45.5	47.5	49.0	50.5	52.5	54.5	57.5	59.5	60.5	61.5	61.5	61.5
Medium — { To	47.4	49.4	51.9	54.4	56.4	58.4	60.9	63.4	64.9	65.4	65.9	65.9	65.9
Tall — More than	47.4	49.4	51.9	54.4	56.4	58.4	60.9	63.4	64.9	65.4	65.9	65.9	65.9

These values have been rounded to the nearest .0 or .5.

TABLE IIC. — ANNUAL GAIN IN MEAN WEIGHT OF SHORT, MEDIUM, AND TALL GIRLS

	AGE, YEARS											
	6-7	7-8	8-9	9-10	10-11	11-12	12-13	13-14	14-15	15-16	16-17	17-18
	GAIN, POUNDS											
Short	4	4	4	5	6	6	12	12	9	8	1	1
Medium	5	6	6	6	7	9	14	9	7	4	2	1
Tall	6	8	9	8	11	13	12	7	4	4	1	1

TABLE III. — HEIGHTS AND WEIGHTS FOR BOYS OVER FIVE YEARS OF AGE [1]

Height,[2] Inches	Age, Years (Weight, Pounds)													Height, Inches
	6	7	8	9	10	11	12	13	14	15	16	17	18	
37.5 — 38.4	34*	34*	34*	—	—	—	—	—	—	—	—	—	—	37.5 — 38.4
38.5 — 39.4	35*	35*	35*	—	—	—	—	—	—	—	—	—	—	38.5 — 39.4
39.5 — 40.4	36*	36*	36*	—	—	—	—	—	—	—	—	—	—	39.5 — 40.4
40.5 — 41.4	38	38*	38*	—	—	—	—	—	—	—	—	—	—	40.5 — 41.4
41.5 — 42.4	39	39*	39*	40*	—	—	—	—	—	—	—	—	—	41.5 — 42.4
42.5 — 43.4	41	41*	41*	42*	—	—	—	—	—	—	—	—	—	42.5 — 43.4
43.5 — 44.4	44	44	44*	44*	45*	—	—	—	—	—	—	—	—	43.5 — 44.4
44.5 — 45.4	46	46	46*	46*	47*	—	—	—	—	—	—	—	—	44.5 — 45.4
45.5 — 46.4	48	48	48	48*	49*	49*	—	—	—	—	—	—	—	45.5 — 46.4
46.5 — 47.4	50	50	50	50*	50*	51*	51*	—	—	—	—	—	—	46.5 — 47.4
47.5 — 48.4	52	53	53	53	53*	54*	54*	—	—	—	—	—	—	47.5 — 48.4
48.5 — 49.4	55	55	55	55	55	55*	56*	—	—	—	—	—	—	48.5 — 49.4
49.5 — 50.4	57*	58	58	58	58	58*	58*	59*	59*	60*	—	—	—	49.5 — 50.4
50.5 — 51.4	60*	61	61	61	61	61	61*	62*	62*	63*	—	—	—	50.5 — 51.4
51.5 — 52.4	63*	63	64	64	64	64	64	64*	65*	66*	—	—	—	51.5 — 52.4
52.5 — 53.4	65*	66*	67	67	67	67	68	68*	69*	70*	—	—	—	52.5 — 53.4
53.5 — 54.4	68*	69*	70	70	70	70	71	71	72*	73*	—	—	—	53.5 — 54.4
54.5 — 55.4	—	71*	72*	72	73	73	74	74	74*	76*	77*	—	—	54.5 — 55.4
55.5 — 56.4	—	74*	75*	76	77	77	77	78	78	80*	81*	—	—	55.5 — 56.4
56.5 — 57.4	—	—	78*	79*	80	81	81	82	83	83*	84*	—	—	56.5 — 57.4

Height (in.)													Height (in.)
57.5 —58.4	82*	83*	84	84	85	85	86	87	88*	96	97*	110*	57.5 —58.4
58.5 —59.4	—	86*	87	88	89	89	90	90	90	103	106*	116*	58.5 —59.4
59.5 —60.4	90*	91*	92	92	93	94	95	96	99	103	111	123	59.5 —60.4
60.5 —61.4	94*	95	96	97	99	100	103	106*	—	121	126	—	60.5 —61.4
61.5 —62.4	97*	100*	101	102	102	103	104	107	111	118	123	—	61.5 —62.4
62.5 —63.4	102*	105*	106	106	107	108	110	113	118	126	—	—	62.5 —63.4
63.5 —64.4	106*	108*	109	109	111	113	115	117	121	126	—	—	63.5 —64.4
64.5 —65.4	110*	112*	114*	117	117	118	120	122	127	131	—	—	64.5 —65.4
65.5 —66.4	113*	115*	117*	119	119	122	125	128	132	136	—	—	65.5 —66.4
66.5 —67.4	—	—	124*	—	128	130	134	136	139	—	—	—	66.5 —67.4
67.5 —68.4	—	—	—	—	134	134	137	141	143	—	—	—	67.5 —68.4
68.5 —69.4	—	—	—	—	137	137	139	143	146	149	—	—	68.5 —69.4
69.5 —70.4	—	—	—	143	143	144	145	148	151	—	—	—	69.5 —70.4
70.5 —71.4	—	—	—	148*	150	151	152	154	—	—	—	—	70.5 —71.4
71.5 —72.4	—	—	—	—	153	155	156	158	—	—	—	—	71.5 —72.4
72.5 —73.4	—	—	—	—	157*	160	162	164	—	—	—	—	72.5 —73.4
73.5 —74.4	—	—	—	—	160*	164	168	170	—	—	—	—	73.5 —74.4

* The starred figures represent values based upon theoretical computations instead of on exact averages.

Age is taken at the nearest birthday; for example, a child is considered 6 years old from 5 years, 6 months to 6 years, 5 months, and 29 days, inclusive.

Weight is taken at the nearest pound.

In these standards a certain percentage of net weight has been included to allow for clothing, except shoes and sweaters, which are removed when weight is taken:

For weight from 35 to 63 pounds, 3.5 per cent of the net weight has been included.

For weight 64 pounds or more, 4 per cent of the net weight has been included.

[1] Prepared by Bird T. Baldwin, Ph.D., Iowa Child Welfare Research Station, State University of Iowa, and Thomas D. Wood, M.D., Teachers College, Columbia University, New York City.

[2] In taking height, stand with heels together and heels, shoulders, and head against the wall. Avoid stretching above a normal height.

TABLE IIIA. — MEAN WEIGHT OF SHORT, MEDIUM, AND TALL BOYS

	AGE, YEARS												
	6	7	8	9	10	11	12	13	14	15	16	17	18
	WEIGHT, POUNDS												
Short . . .	41.2	43.4	46.7	53.1	58.6	64.6	67.2	75.2	84.2	94.1	105.4	118.6	126.5
Medium . .	48.3	53.1	58.2	63.9	70.1	76.5	82.9	91.7	104.9	117.3	129.0	136.2	141.3
Tall . . .	57.8	63.7	75.0	76.3	84.7	92.2	102.3	113.3	128.3	140.7	146.4	152.6	160.1

TABLE IIIB. — RANGE OF HEIGHT OF SHORT, MEDIUM, AND TALL BOYS

	AGE, YEARS												
	6	7	8	9	10	11	12	13	14	15	16	17	18
	HEIGHT, INCHES												
Short — Less than	43.5	45.5	47.5	49.5	51.5	53.5	54.5	56.5	59.0	61.0	63.0	65.0	66.0
Medium — { From .	43.5	45.5	47.5	49.5	51.5	53.5	54.5	56.5	59.0	61.0	63.0	65.0	66.0
Medium — { To .	48.4	50.4	52.4	54.5	56.4	58.4	60.4	62.9	65.9	68.4	69.9	70.9	71.4
Tall — More than	48.4	50.4	52.4	54.4	56.4	58.4	60.4	62.9	65.9	68.4	69.9	70.9	71.4

These values have been rounded to the nearest .0 or .5.

TABLE IIIC. — ANNUAL GAIN IN MEAN WEIGHT OF SHORT, MEDIUM, AND TALL BOYS

	AGE, YEARS											
	6-7	7-8	8-9	9-10	10-11	11-12	12-13	13-14	14-15	15-16	16-17	17-18
	GAIN, POUNDS											
Short	2	3	6	6	6	6	8	9	10	11	13	8
Medium	5	5	6	6	6	6	9	13	12	12	7	5
Tall	6	7	6	8	8	10	11	15	12	6	6	7

Making a weight chart. It may be interesting to make a chart showing your rate of growth over a given period of time. If such a chart is followed, month by month, it will show whether gains are below or above the average for height and age.

To make a weight chart, take a piece of plotting or graph paper marked in squares. Each heavy line is one inch from the next heavy line, and paper with ten small squares to the inch is easiest to work with. On the second heavy line from the lower edge of the paper draw a heavy horizontal line across the paper. On the second heavy line from the left-hand edge of the paper draw a heavy vertical line. As a chart must be made to cover a definite period, decide upon the length of time during which you will follow your weight, as one month, three months, six months, or one year. For purposes of illustration we have used eight months on Charts VI and VII. On the left-hand vertical line, indicate pounds, as in Charts VI and VII, making the range wide enough to include your own weight. Ascertain your weight and mark it with a dot on the left-hand vertical line. Directly below it, in the lower margin of the paper, insert the date at which the weight was taken. At the next weighing, mark your weight on the next heavy vertical line and insert the date of weighing directly beneath it as before. Connect the two weights with a straight line. Record each successive weight on the next-in-order heavy vertical line, and so on. (Weighing days should come at regular intervals so that all squares cover the same length of time.) The line connecting the various weights is a graphic representation of your gains in weight.

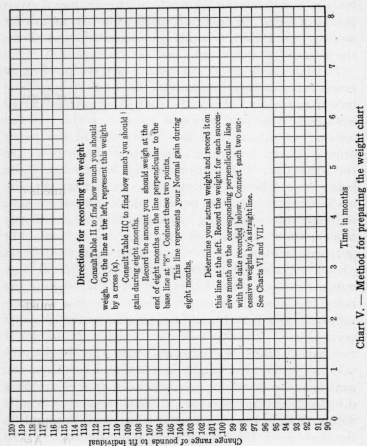

Directions for recording the weight

Consult Table II to find how much you should weigh. On the line at the left, represent this weight by a cross (x).

Consult Table IIC to find how much you should gain during eight months.

Record the amount you should weigh at the end of eight months on the line perpendicular to the base line at "8". Connect these two points.

This line represents your Normal gain during eight months.

Determine your actual weight and record it on this line at the left. Record the weight for each successive month on the corresponding perpendicular line with the date recorded below. Connect each two successive weights by a straight line. See Charts VI and VII.

Chart V. — Method for preparing the weight chart

The average-weight line.   The lines described above tell the story of your own weight.   To compare your gains with the average gain of girls (or boys) of your own age and height, consult Table II and find the average weight for your height and age.   Check this figure with a dot on the left-hand vertical line on the plotting paper.   By means of Table IIC (IIIC for boys), calculate the amount you should normally gain during the next eight months.   Add this amount to your present average weight.   The sum of these two figures represents the weight you may expect to attain at the end of eight months.   Indicate this weight at the right-hand side of the chart (eight squares over if the weight is to be followed for eight months, and if each square is to represent the passage of a month in time).   Connect the two points with a straight line.   This line is the average gain for girls (or boys) of your height and age over a period of eight months.   It is called the average weight line.   If your weight is more than 7 per cent below or more than 15 per cent above this average-weight line, it may be well to carry the safety zone on your chart.

A safety zone.   The weight tables represent the average weight for height of thousands of boys and girls, and, while they may indicate that a person of a certain height and age should weigh a certain definite amount, it would be unreasonable and unsound to conclude that this may be true for everyone.   The weight may run 7 per cent below or as much as 15 per cent above the averages as given in the tables without cause for alarm.   This safety range is sometimes called a **safety zone** and may be graphically shown for any one

individual as in Chart VI.   But when the weight falls
outside such a zone there should be a physical examination to determine the cause, with a careful inspection
of the diet to ascertain whether it contains all the elements needed in the right amounts for normal growth,
for good health, and for a reasonable amount of activity.

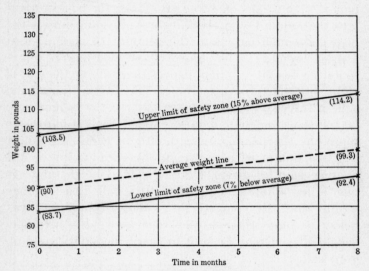

Chart VI. — The safety zone for weight

Representing the safety zone on the chart.   To make
a safety zone on your chart, draw in the average-weight
line as indicated in the preceding paragraph.   Subtract
7 per cent from the average weight of girls (or boys) of
your own height and age as indicated by the left-hand
end of the average-weight line.   Mark the result on the
left-hand vertical line of the weight chart.   Subtract
7 per cent from your expected weight at the end of eight

months as indicated by the right-hand end of the average weight line and mark it on the right-hand side of the weight chart. Connect these two points with a straight line. This line marks the lower limit of the safety zone.

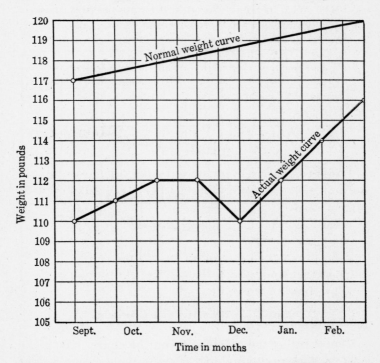

Chart VII. — An actual record kept by a Washington Irving High School girl, age 15 years, 63 inches tall

In a similar way find the upper limit of the safety zone, adding 15 per cent to rather than subtracting 7 per cent from the average weights. Chart VI gives an illustration of a safety zone.

PROBLEMS

1. To ascertain the weight and height of each member of the class:
    Take and record your own weight and height and compare
    it with the average for your age as given in Table II or Table
    III.   What per cent above or below the average are you?
    Are you within a safety zone for weight?

2. To ascertain the average age, weight, and height of the whole
    class:
    Add together the weights of all the members of the class.
    Do the same for the heights; for the ages.   What is the aver-
    age height, weight, and age of the whole class?

Signs Other than Weight as an Indication of Health

Weight is only one factor to be considered in judging
normal physical condition.   Other factors equally important are:

Steady normal gains in weight, month by month

A feeling of vigor

Few, if any, colds or other infections

Good digestion and proper daily elimination

Unobstructed nose breathing

Red and healthy-appearing mucous membrane on
lips and inner eyelids

Sound teeth with healthy gums

A clear skin, not too dry

Good firm muscles with enough subcutaneous fat for
plumpness

Good posture

A firm, energetic step

Bright eyes, rested in appearance

Glossy hair

Quiet sleep, with a feeling of freshness on awaking

A vigorous appetite

Check your own health habits. Below is a form whereby each student may check his or her own observance of the chief health rules. Each is a very important part of the whole, and none may be neglected if best results in terms of health are desired.

HEALTH SCORE CARD			
HEALTH HABIT	SCORE		
	Date	Date	Date
1. A yearly physical examination, with all defects corrected when found . . .			
2. Teeth brushed daily and examined twice a year; all repair work done . . .			
3. Proper hours of sleep, with windows open			
4. One or more hours out of doors daily .			
5. At least one half hour in the sun each pleasant day			
6. One to two hours of exercise daily . .			
7. Regular bowel movements			
8. Good posture			
9. Three regular and appropriate meals a day.			
10. Six to eight glasses of water daily . .			
Total.................................			

Each point scores 10; a perfect score is 100.

PROBLEMS

3. To start a chart record of your weight:

    Secure a piece of plotting or graph paper and mark it like the illustration in Chart VI. On this sheet draw a line representing the average weight and increase in weight for a person of your age and height, and record with dots your present weight and height. On the first of each month determine your weight, and place a dot in its respective place on the chart, connecting the dots with a straight line. Girls who are more than 7 per cent below or 15 per cent above average weight should carry a safety zone on their charts. (Chart VII represents the actual record kept by a girl at the Washington Irving High School, New York City.)

4. Select a seven- or eight-year-old child of your acquaintance and start a chart of its weight. (As you progress in the course you may be able to give helpful suggestions regarding the diet of the child.)

5. To check your own health habits:

    Each point on the Health Score Card scores ten. A perfect score is one hundred. What is your score? Keep this record in your note book, and recheck your health habits at the end of the term.

QUESTIONS

1. Health is essential for happiness. What is necessary for good health? When should you begin to pay attention to your health? Why?

2. What has food to do with our activity? What has food to do with body temperature?

3. How do we know that food influences growth?

4. At what age do boys and girls increase in weight most rapidly? How much should you gain in weight for the next twelve months if you are of average weight?

5. What has weight to do with physical fitness? In your experience have you found this to be true?

6. Enumerate other factors which are necessary for good nutrition.

7. Completion test:

For good health —— —— is necessary.

Proper food is necessary for ——, ——, ——.

Besides food, ——, ——, ——, ——, ——, —— are controlling factors in health.

Physical fitness is often indicated by —— and ——.

REFERENCES

For students:

ROSE, MARY S. *Feeding the Family*, third edition, Chapter I, pages 1 to 3. The Macmillan Company (1929).

For teachers:

ROSE, MARY S. *Feeding the Family*, third edition, Chapter I. The Macmillan Company (1929).

——. *Foundations of Nutrition*, Chapter I, Chapter II, and pages 304 to 306. The Macmillan Company (1927).

SHERMAN, H. C. *Chemistry of Food and Nutrition*, third edition, Chapter XX. The Macmillan Company (1926).

CHAPTER II

THE ENERGY VALUE OF FOODS

WE eat to supply real needs, needs greater than the mere satisfying of the appetite. For a wise selection of foods it is necessary to know of what foods are made, to know what and how much food any given individual may need under certain circumstances, and to know how to calculate the amount of food to provide for these needs. The Calorie is a convenient measure in adjusting food to requirement.

Selection of food should not be left to chance. For many years crops and livestock have been carefully fed to produce the best results, and now men and women are realizing the advantages to be derived in terms of better health, greater endurance, and more vigor, by selecting their own food to meet their individual needs. There is a chance, to be sure, that a person may keep strong and healthy while following the dictates of appetite, but there is also danger in this haphazard method, for frequently the appetite has been pampered and abused until it can no longer be trusted to protect its owner from errors in diet.

For an intelligent adjustment of food to personal requirement to provide for normal growth, health, and energy, it is necessary to know about the composition of foods and the needs of the body, and to have some means of measuring food values. And as a much larger amount of food is used to provide energy for work and for keeping us warm than for any other purpose, we begin our acquaintance with foods by considering them first as a source of energy. Other needs are much more likely to be supplied in sufficient amounts if energy is adequate.

THE FUEL VALUE OF FOODS

The Calorie. The fuel value of a food is a measure of the energy it will produce. We are familiar with, and appreciate the value of, the burning of coal which produces heat to keep us warm on cold days in winter, or which will produce power to make a steam engine run. Perhaps we are not so familiar with the fact that food burned in the body is the source of the energy which keeps us warm internally and gives us power to do work. The amount of heat any given food will produce outside of the body may be measured in

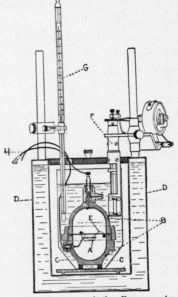

Courtesy of the Emerson Apparatus Co., Boston, Mass.

Illustration No. 1. — Diagram of a Bomb Calorimeter

A. Platinum dish holding food sample of which the energy value is to be determined
B. Bomb filled with pure oxygen enclosing food sample
C. Can of water surrounding the bomb
D. Double-walled insulating jacket
E. Fuse to be ignited by an electric current
F. Motor-driven water stirrer
G. Thermometer
H. Electric wires through which current is sent to the fuse for the purpose of igniting it

an apparatus called a **bomb calorimeter,** as shown in Illustration No. 1. This makes it possible to tell how much energy each food will provide in the body, and thus to judge how much food we need during the day. For the sake of convenience it is necessary to have a name to designate a definite amount of heat produced by foods, just as we have other units of measure. The unit of heat is called a **Calorie.**[1]

100-Calorie portions. A piece of good coal weighing 0.6 ounce will when burned yield 100 Calories. A potato weighing 5.3 ounces will give the same amount of heat. If an apple weighing 7.5 ounces were burned it would produce 100 Calories; a tablespoon of oil weighing 0.4 ounce, 0.9 to 1.0 ounce of sugar, starch, dry cereal, or flour, 1.4 ounces of bread, about 10 ounces of carrots, and 24 ounces of lettuce will each produce the same amount of heat, or 100 Calories. It is comparatively easy to find a potato weighing 5.3 ounces, or an apple weighing 7.5 ounces,each of which will give 100 Calories; but it would be extremely difficult to weigh the amount of either the potato or the apple that would give one Calorie. For convenience, then, foods are frequently measured in 100-Calorie portions instead of in smaller quantities.

WEIGHING 100-CALORIE PORTIONS

Scales. The laboratory should be equipped with Harvard Trip scales or some other accurate scales for weighing food. Either the metric or the avoirdupois system of weights, or both, may be used.

---

[1] The word Calorie is used to designate the large calorie, or the amount of heat required to raise the temperature of one kilogram of water one degree centigrade.

PROBLEMS

6. To learn to use the scales:

Place the scales directly in front of you with the box of weights in front of the scales. Balance the scales by means of the small balance wheel until the pointer swings as far to the left as to the right, and when at rest is in the center. Use a pair of tweezers to remove the weights from the box. (If the weights are touched with the hands, grasp them by the handles only.) Replace the weights in the box as soon as you have finished weighing.

The articles to be weighed should be placed on the left side of the scales, the weights on the right. Filter paper or small pieces of paraffin paper should be used under the food. If pieces of paper of equal weight are placed on either side of the scales, the scales will not have to be readjusted. When a saucer or tin cup is used for holding any food, place one of corresponding size on the side with the weights and only slight adjustment will be necessary.

Find the weight of the tablespoon, the teaspoon, tin cup, white bowls, saucer, and china cup in the laboratory desk. Record these weights in your notebook.

Weigh out 28.35 grams[1] of flour. How many ounces have you? Measure the quantity with a tablespoon.

Weigh one cup of sugar. How many grams in one cup of sugar? How many ounces? What proportion of a pound is it?

100-Calorie Portions

The tables on pages 31 to 39 contain many foods with the weights of 100-Calorie portions of food as purchased. These foods are to be weighed and measured. Each pupil should have a notebook ruled as shown below. Copy the name of the food with the corresponding weights from the book. Weigh each food carefully

---

[1] In practice it is usually sufficient to weigh to the nearest gram.

and measure it by a standard tablespoon or cup. It is important that each pupil do the weighing and measuring herself so that she may become familiar with the measurements. If there are no scales in the laboratory, the weighing will have to be omitted, but the foods should be carefully measured according to the quantities given in the tables. The main object is to get a visual idea of the 100-Calorie portions. Find out the local price per pound and calculate the cost of the portion. Record the results in the notebook.

Rule the notebook as follows:

100-CALORIE PORTIONS

APPROXIMATE WEIGHT AND MEASURE OF THE 100-CALORIE POR-
TION OF EACH OF THE COMMON GRAIN PRODUCTS AS ORDI-
NARILY PURCHASED

FOOD	CALORIES	WEIGHT		MEASURE	COST	
		Grams	Ounces		100 Calories	Pound
Barley	100	28	1.0	3 tbsp.	—	—

PROBLEMS [1]

7. To find the measure of the 100-Calorie portion of each of the common grain products:

Weigh out the specified amount of each of the grain products given in Table IV. Find the measure and record results in your notebook. Record the cost per pound and per 100-Calorie portion.

[1] The abbreviations used throughout the text of this book are as follows: tbsp. for tablespoon; tsp. for teaspoon; c. for cup.

8. To find the measure of the 100-Calorie portion of each of the common fruits:

   Weigh out the specified amount of each of the fruits given in Table V, find the measure, and record the results in your notebook. Find and record the cost of each. Arrange according to cost and compare them.

9. To find the measure of the 100-Calorie portion of each of the common vegetables:

   Weigh out the specified amount of each of the vegetables given in Table VI and record the quantity in your notebook. Can you account for the different amounts of the various vegetables needed to give 100 Calories?

   Divide the 100-Calorie portion of each vegetable into average-sized servings and record the number.

TABLE IV. — APPROXIMATE WEIGHT AND MEASURE OF THE 100-CALORIE PORTION OF EACH OF THE COMMON GRAIN PRODUCTS AS ORDINARILY PURCHASED (Based on Rose's *Laboratory Handbook for Dietetics* and *Feeding the Family*)

| FOOD — GRAIN PRODUCTS | CALO-RIES | WEIGHT | | MEASURE |
		Grams	Ounces	
Barley, pearl . . .	100	28	1.0	3 tbsp.
Bread, brown . . .	100	51	1.8	¾ in. slice, 3 in. diam.
Bread, graham . .	100	40	1.4	3 slices, ⅜ in. ×2 in. ×3¼ in.
Bread, rye	100	39	1.4	1⅓ slices, 3½ in. ×4 in. ×½ in.
Bread, white . . .	100	39	1.3	2 slices, 2½ in. ×2¾ in. ×¼ in.
Bread, whole wheat .	100	40	1.4	2 slices, 3 in. ×3½ in. ×½ in.
Cornflakes	100	28	1.0	1¼ cups
Cornmeal	100	28	1.0	3 tbsp.
Cornstarch	100	28	1.0	3 tbsp.
Crackers, graham . .	100	23	0.8	2 crackers
Crackers, saltines . .	100	23	0.8	6 crackers
Crackers, soda . .	100	26	0.9	4 crackers

TABLE IV — *Continued*

Food—Grain Products	Calories	Weight		Measure
		Grams	Ounces	
Farina	100	28	1.0	3 tbsp.
Flour, graham . . .	100	28	1.0	3 tbsp.
Flour, white . . .	100	28	1.0	4 tbsp.
Flour, entire wheat .	100	28	1.0	3 tbsp.
Grapenuts	100	28	1.0	3 tbsp.
Hominy	100	28	1.0	$3\frac{1}{2}$ tbsp.
Macaroni	100	28	1.0	$\frac{1}{4}$ cup
Oats, rolled . . .	100	28	1.0	$\frac{1}{3}$ cup
Rice	100	28	1.0	2 tbsp.
Rice, puffed . . .	100	28	1.0	$1\frac{1}{3}$ cups
Tapioca	100	28	1.0	3 tbsp.
Triscuit	100	28	1.0	4 triscuits, 2 in. sq.
Shredded wheat . .	100	26	0.9	1 biscuit
Wheat, puffed . . .	100	28	1.0	2 cups
Zwieback	100	23	0.8	3 pieces, $3\frac{1}{4}$ in. $\times$ $\frac{1}{2}$ in. $\times 1\frac{1}{4}$ in.

TABLE V. — Approximate Weight and Measure of the 100-Calorie Portion of Each of the Common Fruits as Ordinarily Purchased (Based on Rose's *Laboratory Handbook for Dietetics*)

Food — Fruits	Calories	Weight		Measure
		Grams	Ounces	
Fruit, dried				
Apples	100	34	1.2	$\frac{1}{2}$ cup
Apricots	100	37	1.3	9 halves
Citron	100	31	1.1	Piece $1\frac{1}{4}$ in. $\times$ 1 in. $\times$ 1 in.
Currants	100	31	1.1	$\frac{1}{4}$ cup
Dates	100	31	1.1	$4\frac{1}{2}$ dates
Figs	100	31	1.1	$1\frac{1}{2}$ large figs

TABLE V — *Continued*

| Food — Fruits | Calories | Weight | | Measure |
		Grams	Ounces	
Prunes . . .	100	40	1.4	4 medium prunes
Raisins . . .	100	31	1.1	¼ cup
Fruit, fresh				
Apples . . .	100	213	7.5	1 large apple
Apricots, canned .	100	137	4.8	3 large halves and 2 tbsp. of juice
Avocado				
(alligator pear) . .	100	117	4.1	½ medium
Bananas . . .	100	156	5.5	1 large banana
Blackberries . .	100	170	6.0	½ cup, 50 berries
Cherries, stoned .	100	128	4.5	1 cup
Cranberries . .	100	215	7.6	2 cups
Currants . . .	100	170	6.0	1½ cups
Figs, fresh . .	100	123	4.3	3 small
Grapes, Concord .	100	142	5.0	1 large bunch grapes
Grape juice . .	100	102	3.6	½ cup
Huckleberries . .	100	133	4.7	1 cup
Lemons . . .	100	323	11.4	3 large lemons
Muskmelon . .	100	510	18.0	1 medium sized
Olives, green .	100	45	1.6	6 to 8 olives
Oranges . . .	100	270	9.5	1 large orange
Orange juice .	100	230	8.2	1 cup
Peaches, fresh . .	100	295	10.5	3 medium sized peaches
Peaches, canned .	100	213	7.5	2 halves with 3 tbsp. juice
Pears . . .	100	180	6.3	1 large pear
Plums . . .	100	125	4.4	3 to 4 large plums
Pineapple, fresh .	100	232	8.2	2 slices, 1 in. thick
Pineapple, canned .	100	65	2.3	1 slice with 3 tbsp. juice or ¼ cup shredded
Raspberries . .	100	150	5.3	1⅛ cup
Rhubarb . . .	100	434	15.3	4 cups, cut in small pieces
Strawberries . .	100	255	9.0	1⅓ cups
Watermelon				
(edible part) . .	100	331	11.7	¾ in. slice, 6 in. diam.

TABLE VI. — APPROXIMATE WEIGHT AND MEASURE OF THE 100-CALORIE PORTION OF EACH OF THE COMMON VEGETABLES AS ORDINARILY PURCHASED (Based on Rose's *Laboratory Handbook for Dietetics* and *Feeding the Family*)

FOOD — VEGETABLES	CALORIES	Weight		MEASURE
		Grams	Ounces	
Asparagus, fresh . .	100	450	15.9	20 stalks, 8 in. long
Asparagus, canned .	100	346	12.0	15 large stalks, 5½ in. long
Beans, baked, canned	100	78	2.7	⅓ cup
Beans, Lima, fresh, shelled . . .	100	80	2.9	½ c.
Beans, Lima, dried .	100	28	1.0	2 tbsp.
Beans, string . .	100	240	8.5	2¼ cups, cut in pieces
Beans, white, dried .	100	28	1.0	2 tbsp.
Beets	100	218	7.7	4 beets, 2 in. diam.
Brussels sprouts . .	100	476	16.7	1 quart box
Cabbage	100	318	11.2	5 cups, shredded
Carrots	100	285	10.1	4 to 5 young carrots
Cauliflower . . .	100	325	11.5	1 small head
Celery	100	540	19.1	4 cups, cut in pieces
Corn on cob . . .	100	255	9.0	2 ears, 6 in. long
Corn, canned . . .	100	102	3.6	⅓ cup
Cucumbers	100	666	23.5	2½ cucumbers, 7 in. long
Dandelion greens, cooked . . .	100	164	5.8	2⅓ cups
Eggplant	100	358	12.6	6 slices, 4 in. diam.× ½ in. thick
Endive	100	714	25.1	14 stalks, 5¾ in. long
Kale, cooked . . .	100	226	8.0	2⅓ cups
Lentils, dried . . .	100	28	1.0	2½ tbsp.
Lettuce	100	525	18.5	2 large heads
Mushrooms . . .	100	225	7.9	22 mushrooms, 1 in. diam.
Okra	100	285	10.0	25 to 30 pods
Onions	100	204	7.2	3 to 4 medium onions
Parsnips	100	198	7.0	2 medium parsnips
Peas, fresh	100	100	3.5	¾ cup, shelled
Peas, canned . . .	100	125	4.4	¾ cup
Peas, split	100	28	1.0	2⅙ tbsp.

TABLE VI — *Continued*

FOOD — VEGETABLES	CALO-RIES	Grams	Ounces	MEASURE
Peppers, green . . .	100	386	13.6	5 peppers, $3\frac{1}{2}$ in. long
Potatoes, sweet . .	100	102	3.6	$\frac{1}{2}$ potato, medium
Potatoes, white . .	100	150	5.3	1 medium white potato
Potato chips, white .	100	18	0.6	8 to 10 large pieces
Radishes	100	340	12.0	36 small radishes
Spinach	100	417	14.7	3 cups
Spinach, cooked and chopped	100	530	18.7	$2\frac{1}{2}$ cups
Squash, Hubbard, cooked	100	217	7.7	1 cup, scant
Squash, summer . .	100	443	15.6	$\frac{1}{2}$ squash, 5 in. diam.
Succotash, canned .	100	102	3.6	$\frac{1}{3}$ cup
Tomatoes, fresh . .	100	440	15.5	2 to 3 medium tomatoes
Tomatoes, canned .	100	442	15.6	$1\frac{3}{4}$ cups
Turnips	100	369	13.0	2 cups, cut in cubes

TABLE VII. — APPROXIMATE WEIGHT AND MEASURE OF THE 100-CALORIE PORTION OF THE VARIOUS DAIRY PRODUCTS AND SOME FATS (Based on Rose's *Laboratory Handbook for Dietetics* and *Feeding the Family*)

FOOD — DAIRY PRODUCTS, FATS, AND EGGS	CALO-RIES	Grams	Ounces	MEASURE
Bacon fat	100	11	0.4	1 tbsp.
Beef drippings . . .	100	11	0.4	1 tbsp.
Butter	100	14	0.5	1 tbsp. (scant)
Buttermilk	100	285	10.0	$1\frac{1}{8}$ c.
Cheese, American . .	100	23	0.8	$1\frac{1}{8}$ in. cube
Cottage	100	91	3.2	$5\frac{1}{2}$ tbsp.
Cream	100	26	0.9	piece 2 in. $\times$ 1 in. $\times \frac{3}{8}$ in.
Swiss	100	23	0.8	$1\frac{1}{2}$ in. cube
Cod-liver oil . . .	100	11	0.4	1 tbsp.
Cotton seed oil . .	100	11	0.4	1 tbsp.

TABLE VI — *Continued*

Food — Dairy Products, Fats, and Eggs	Calories	Weight		Measure
		Grams	Ounces	
Cream, thin (18%)	100	51	1.8	¼ c.
Cream, thick (40%)	100	26	0.9	1⅓ tbsp.
Cream, whipped	100	26	0.9	2 tbsp.
Crisco	100	11	0.4	1 tbsp.
Eggs in shell	100	77	2.7	1⅓ egg
Egg white	100	196	6.9	7 whites
Egg yolk	100	28	1.0	2 yolks
Lard	100	11	0.4	1 tbsp.
Mayonnaise dressing	100	14	0.5	1 tbsp.
Milk, whole	100	145	5.1	⅝ c.
Condensed (sweetened)	100	31	1.1	1½ tbsp.
Condensed (unsweetened)	100	60	2.1	3¾ tbsp.
Malted	100	26	0.9	3 tbsp.
Powdered — whole	100	23	0.8	
Powdered — skimmed	100	28	1.0	
Skimmed	100	272	9.6	1⅞ c.
Top milk	100	75	2.7	¼ c.
Oleomargarine	100	11	0.4	1 tbsp.
Olive oil	100	11	0.4	1 tbsp.
Suet (rendered)	100	11	0.4	1 tbsp.

PROBLEMS

10. To find the measure of the 100-Calorie portion of the various dairy products and some fats:

Weigh out the specified amounts of the foods given in Table VII, measure, and record the results.

11. To compare the fuel value and cost of various foods:

Place the 100-Calorie portions of butter, oatmeal, bananas, prunes, and potatoes together. Which of these foods supplies fuel in the most concentrated form?

Find the cost of each of these 100-Calorie portions. Which supplies fuel in the most economical form?

TABLE VIII. — APPROXIMATE WEIGHT AND MEASURE OF THE 100-CALORIE PORTION OF VARIOUS KINDS OF MEAT AND FISH (Based on Rose's *Laboratory Handbook for Dietetics* and *Feeding the Family*)

FOOD — MEAT AND FISH	CALORIES	WEIGHT		MEASURE
		Grams	Ounces	
Meat				
Beef, corned, boiled	100	85	3.0	slice $4\frac{1}{2}$ in. × $1\frac{1}{2}$ in. × $\frac{5}{6}$ in.
Dried	100	57	2.0	4 thin slices, 4 in. × 5 in.
Hamburg steak	100	57	2.0	1 cake $2\frac{1}{2}$ in. diam. × $\frac{7}{8}$ in. thick
Lean meat, uncooked	100	64	2.3	slice $2\frac{3}{4}$ in. × $1\frac{1}{2}$ in. × $\frac{3}{4}$ in.
Liver, broiled and ground	100	59	2.1	$\frac{1}{2}$ cup
Sirloin, lean, broiled	100	57	2.0	slice 2 in. × $1\frac{1}{2}$ in. × $\frac{3}{4}$ in.
Rib, roasted	100	45	1.6	slice 5 in. × $2\frac{1}{2}$ in. × $\frac{1}{4}$ in.
Round, broiled	100	57	2.0	slice 4 in. × 3 in. × $1\frac{1}{8}$ in.
Bologna sausage	100	43	1.5	slice $2\frac{1}{8}$ in. diam.; $\frac{1}{2}$ in. thick
Chicken, broiled	100	74	2.6	slice 4 in. × $2\frac{1}{2}$ in. × $\frac{1}{8}$ in.
Chicken, canned	100	44	1.5	$\frac{1}{4}$ cup
Frankfurters	100	31	1.1	1 frankfurter, $4\frac{1}{2}$ in. long
Gelatin	100	27	1.0	$3\frac{2}{5}$ tablespoons
Lamb chops	100	45	1.6	1 chop, 2 in. × 2 in. × $\frac{1}{2}$ in.
Lamb, leg, roast	100	51	1.8	slice, $3\frac{1}{2}$ in. × $4\frac{1}{2}$ in. × $\frac{1}{8}$ in.
Liver	100	60	2.1	slice 2 in. × $2\frac{3}{4}$ in. × $\frac{1}{4}$ in.
Mutton, roasted	100	34	1.2	slice 3 in. × $3\frac{3}{4}$ in. × $\frac{1}{8}$ in.
Pork, bacon, fried	100	14	0.5	4-5 small slices
Ham, boiled	100	37	1.3	slice $4\frac{3}{4}$ in. × 4 in. × $\frac{1}{8}$ in.
Sausage, fried	100	31	1.1	$1\frac{2}{3}$ sausage 3 in. × $\frac{3}{4}$ in.
Turkey, roasted	100	37	1.3	slice 4 in. × $2\frac{1}{2}$ in. × $\frac{1}{8}$ in.
Veal	100	65	2.3	slice 2 in. × $2\frac{3}{4}$ in. × $\frac{1}{8}$ in.
Veal liver, pan broiled	100	60	2.1	slice $3\frac{1}{2}$ in. × $2\frac{1}{2}$ in. × $\frac{3}{8}$ in.
Fish				
Bluefish	100	68	2.4	piece 3 in. × 3 in. × $\frac{1}{2}$ in.
Clams, raw	100	215	7.6	6 clams or $\frac{1}{2}$ c.
Halibut steak, broiled	100	85	3.0	piece 3 in. × $2\frac{1}{4}$ in. × 1 in.
Lobster, canned	100	119	4.2	$\frac{3}{4}$ cup
Mackerel, Spanish, broiled	100	74	2.6	piece 3 in. × $2\frac{1}{2}$ in. × 1 in.
Oysters, raw	100	204	7.2	6 to 12 oysters, $\frac{2}{3}$ c.

TABLE VIII — *Continued*

FOOD — MEAT AND FISH	CALO-RIES	WEIGHT		MEASURE
		Grams	Ounces	
Salmon, canned .	100	51	1.8	½ c.
Sardines, canned .	100	48	1.7	3 to 6 sardines
Scallops, raw . .	100	136	4.8	¾ c.
Shrimps, raw . .	100	91	3.2	½ c.
Tuna fish, canned .	100	79	2.8	½ c.

PROBLEMS

12. To find the measure of the 100-Calorie portion of various kinds of meat and fish:

Weigh out the specified amount of each of the various kinds of meat and fish given in Table VIII. Record the measure in your notebook. Find and record the cost. Compare and arrange them according to cost.

TABLE IX. — APPROXIMATE WEIGHT AND MEASURE OF THE 100-CALORIE PORTION OF SOME COMMON NUTS; EDIBLE PORTION (Based on Rose's *Laboratory Handbook for Dietetics* and *Feeding the Family*)

FOOD — NUTS	CALO-RIES	WEIGHT		MEASURE
		Grams	Ounces	
Almonds, shelled . .	100	14	0.5	12 to 15 nuts
Almonds, salted . .	100	15	0.5	10 to 12 nuts
Brazil nuts, shelled .	100	14	0.5	2 nuts
Butternuts, shelled .	100	14	0.5	4 to 5 nuts
Coconut, prepared . .	100	17	0.6	⅙ c.
Chestnuts, Italian .	100	43	1.5	7 nuts
Filberts, shelled . .	100	14	0.5	8 to 10 nuts
Hickory nuts, shelled .	100	14	0.5	15 to 16 nuts
Peanuts, shelled . .	100	17	0.6	20 to 24 (single)
Peanut butter . .	100	17	0.6	2½ tsp.
Pecans, shelled . .	100	14	0.5	12 (single)
Pine nuts, shelled . .	100	17	0.6	¼ c.
Walnuts, English shelled	100	14	0.5	8 to 16 nuts

PROBLEMS

13. To find the measure of the 100-Calorie portion of some common nuts:

Weigh out the specified amount of each of the nuts given in Table IX. Record the measure in your notebook. Find and record the cost.

Compare the size and cost of these 100-Calorie portions with those of meat and fish. Which is the cheaper source of fuel? What advantages have nuts over meat and fish?

TABLE X. — APPROXIMATE WEIGHT AND MEASURE OF THE 100-CALORIE PORTION OF CHLCOLATE, VARIOUS SWEETS, AND SOME COMMON SUGARS (Based on Rose's *Feeding the Family* and *Laboratory Handbook for Dietetics*)

FOOD — CHOCOLATE, SWEETS, ETC.	CALO-RIES	Grams	Ounces	MEASURE
Cherries, candied	100	28	1.0	10 candied cherries
Chocolate, milk, sweetened	100	20	0.7	piece $2\frac{1}{4}$ in. $\times$ 1 in. $\times \frac{1}{8}$ in.
Chocolate, unsweetened	100	17	0.6	piece $\frac{3}{4}$ in. $\times 1\frac{1}{4}$ in. $\times \frac{7}{8}$ in.
Cocoa	100	20	0.7	$3\frac{1}{2}$ tbsp.
Corn syrup	100	43	1.5	$1\frac{3}{4}$ tbsp.
Ginger, crystallized	100	28	1.0	6 pieces, $1\frac{1}{2}$ in. $\times \frac{3}{4}$ in. $\times \frac{1}{4}$ in.
Gumdrops	100	29	1.0	3 large or 25 very small
Honey	100	31	1.1	1 tbsp.
Marshmallows	100	30	1.0	5 pieces, $1\frac{1}{4}$ in. diam.
Maple syrup	100	34	1.2	$1\frac{1}{2}$ tbsp.
Maple sugar	100	31	1.1	4 tbsp.
Molasses	100	34	1.2	$1\frac{1}{2}$ tbsp.
Sugar, brown	100	26	0.9	2 tbsp.
Sugar, granulated	100	26	0.9	2 tbsp.
Sugar, loaf	100	26	0.9	$3\frac{1}{2}$ tbsp.
Sugar, powdered	100	26	0.9	2 tbsp.
White icing (with egg)	100	28	1.0	$2\frac{1}{2}$ tbsp.

PROBLEMS

14. To find the measure of the 100-Calorie portion of chocolate, various sweets, and some common sugars:

   Weigh out the specified amount of each of the foods given in Table X. Measure the quantity of each and record the results. Compare these results with those from the weighing of vegetables, fruits, and fats.

15. To select a luncheon from the 100-Calorie portions:

   From the various foods weighed select an attractive luncheon which shall consist of from 600 to 700 Calories. Calculate the cost.

16. Arrange another luncheon of the same food value as that in Problem 15, selecting from the 100-Calorie portions a very economical combination, containing variety. The luncheon should be suited to the needs of the one for whom it is intended.

A COMPARISON OF THE ENERGY VALUE OF DIFFERENT FOODS

Fats and oils are the most concentrated sources of energy. During the weighing process it must have been noted that it takes more of some foods than of others to produce 100 Calories. One reason for this difference is the amount of water in the structure of the food. Celery and lettuce, for instance, contain so much water that it takes over one pound of each to give the same amount of energy as 0.4 ounce, or one tablespoonful, of clear fat. Oil, lard, sugar, starch, and gelatin, which is a pure protein, are comparatively water-free, but still there is a difference in the amount of these substances required to give 100 Calories; while it takes only one tablespoonful of fat or oil to give this amount of energy, it requires a scant two tablespoonfuls of sugar, three tablespoonfuls of starch, and almost three and one half tablespoonfuls of gelatin to give 100 Calories. Thus it will be seen that fats and oils are more concentrated sources of energy than either sugars, starches, or gelatin, and are therefore the most concentrated sources of energy among foods.

QUESTIONS

1. What arguments other than those in this chapter can you give to support the statement, "The selection of food should not be left to chance"?

2. In order to plan meals intelligently, what must we know about foods?

3. Most of the foods that we eat supply energy. How is this food energy measured? What is the name of the unit used in measuring energy in foods?

4. What is meant by a 100-Calorie portion of food? Name ten foods which most of us eat every day, telling how much it takes of each to give 100 Calories.

5. Completion test.
    One of the greatest needs of the body is ——.
    Of the foods weighed those which supply energy in the most concentrated forms are —— and ——.
    Foods which supply energy in the most economical forms are —— and ——.
    It takes —— tomatoes to give 50 Calories.
    It takes —— leaves of lettuce to give 10 Calories.
    It takes —— tablespoonfuls of mayonnaise to give 100 Calories.
    It takes —— saltines to give 100 Calories.
    It takes —— —— of cheese to give 100 Calories.
    The above forms a —— of —— Calories.

REFERENCES

For students:

ROSE, MARY S., *Feeding the Family*, third edition, Chapter I, pages 4 to 11; Appendix, Table I, pages 348 to 383. The Macmillan Company (1929).

For teachers:

ROSE, MARY S., *Foundations of Nutrition*, Chapters II and III. The Macmillan Company (1927).

——. *Laboratory Handbook for Dietetics*, third edition, Part II, pages 33 to 40; 58 to 94. The Macmillan Company (1929).

SHERMAN, H. C. *Chemistry of Food and Nutrition*, third edition, Chapters II and III. The Macmillan Company (1926).

CHAPTER III

ENERGY REQUIREMENTS OF INDIVIDUALS

THE mechanism of the body is like a delicate machine that needs thoughtful attention; its engine cannot be stopped for an overhauling. Repairs must be made while the heart is still beating and the blood circulating.

The energy required by boys and girls, men and women, is measured in Calories, as is the fuel value of foods. The amount required, or the number of Calories needed, varies with age, size, activity, and climate and temperature.

THE BODY, A HUMAN ENGINE

Each boy and girl may become a skilled engineer. The engineer who knows when to add more fuel to the fire under his engine, who oils this rod and that wheel at proper intervals, who opens this draft or closes that one at the right time, and who avoids accidents by the careful repairing of his engine is a skilled workman. But intricate as the work of the engineer may seem, each boy or girl has, in his or her hands, the control of a far more delicate piece of mechanism than the ordinary engine, and one that requires much more skill and intelligence to handle if the best results are to be obtained.

Extra fuel may be stored in the body. We burn food (fuel) to obtain the energy that makes it possible for us to work, but if on any given day the human engine receives more than enough fuel food to supply the energy needed for that particular day, the extra amount may be stored in the tissues in the form of fat which may be used later in case of an emergency. The reserve thus stored will provide excess fuel which may be used during very cold days in winter, or it may be useful in "unexpected happenings" during any part of the year. It is always well to have a reserve supply, as is illustrated by the following incident:

Two girls started in an automobile for a town ten miles away. When half way there the gasoline gave out. As the car refused to go without fuel the girls had to walk, thus needing an unforeseen supply of body fuel. One of them completed the journey without much fatigue, because she had a reserve supply of fuel in her tissues, a supply that had been accumulating from day to day. The other girl arrived at her destination too, but much exhausted. She had not been eating the kind of food that had allowed her tissues to fortify themselves against the unexpected. "If she had no reserve, then how could she walk any more than the automobile could go?" you ask. She did what no automobile can do; she borrowed her energy from the body tissues themselves. In other words, she burned the "walls of her house" for energy, but in so doing she weakened the tissues and made them more susceptible to disease.

Repairs and replacement are necessary. The human engine wears out, but its repairing, in the hands of a competent engineer, should take place automatically, even while one is studying or playing tennis. Sometimes we are "laid up for repairs" because of illness, but even then repairing must be done while the heart is beating and the blood circulating, and while we are breathing. These motions could not be discontinued for more than a few seconds without fatal results. The work done by the internal organs requires energy just as truly as the swinging of an ax, and fuel must be produced every minute to supply it. The food we eat contains materials for repairing and regulating as well as fuel. Our skill as engineers lies in our ability to provide the proper foods which shall contain not only fuel but building and regulating materials for all the needs, so that we may be in good condition every day. If the word "repair" seems to you to imply that an injury has been done, you may speak of the normal process as one of "replacement" instead. Another phrase used is "exchange of material."

THE AMOUNT OF ENERGY NEEDED BY THE HUMAN ENGINE

The energy required is measured in Calories. Although the needs of the body are varied, we usually speak of them in terms of energy used in doing work and in keeping the body warm.

For every bit of work done there is a certain amount of heat produced, which incidentally keeps us warm. Everyone must have had the experience of feeling increasingly warmer while working rapidly. The harder we work, the more heat is produced, for the heat is in proportion to the work done. If all this heat were to stay bottled up inside, the temperature of the body would quickly rise above what we could endure. But, fortunately for us, we are kept at a nearly constant temperature internally, regardless of the weather outside, because any excess heat above a certain amount is given off through the skin and from the lungs.

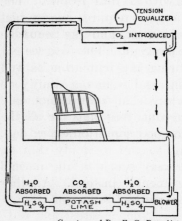

Courtesy of Dr. F. G. Benedict

Illustration No. 2. — One type of respiration calorimeter

Water is absorbed by the sulphuric acid (H_2So_4) and carbon dioxide (CO_2) by the potash lime. The blower keeps the air in circulation as indicated by the arrows.

The excess heat given off may be collected, measured, and used as an index of the energy being produced ("transformed"). This is done by placing the person who is to serve as a subject for the experiment in an air-tight chamber where all conditions are carefully controlled, all heat given off is collected, and the amount of heat is determined. This device for measuring heat is called a calorimeter, meaning that it measures heat in terms of Calories. A diagram of a calorimeter is given in Illustration No. 2.

The Amount of Energy Varies with Conditions

It has been found by repeating such experiments on hundreds of people that the amount of heat given off under the same conditions is very nearly the same for all individuals of the same age and size, but that it increases in proportion to the size and activity of the individual, and is considerably influenced by age. This gives us confidence in using it as a basis for estimating the number of Calories needed by different people under varying conditions.

Influence of activity on the amount of energy needed. The amount of heat given off during different degrees of activity has been studied by several scientists, notably Atwater and Benedict, Lusk, and others. Many of their experiments have been made in the calorimeter, where all the conditions were controlled, and the effect of light, moderate, and vigorous exercise was studied by means of a stationary bicycle.

It was found that when a man is lying on a flat surface apparently motionless there is still considerable heat given off. The work being done to produce the heat consists of the internal processes, such as breathing and the circulation of the blood. This condition represents the lowest amount of work a healthy man can be doing when awake, and the energy needed for these processes is often spoken of as the **basal** requirement. As soon, however, as the person raises his head, or his arm, or his hand, or moves his body in any way, the amount of heat produced increases, and this increase in heat is a measure of the energy used in moving.

The heat produced is not only in proportion to the amount of muscular work done, but is also in proportion to the size of the muscles used in working. For example, the swinging of the arm of a large man will produce more heat than an equally vigorous, similar motion of a smaller man, or of an equally rapid motion of the fingers of the same man.

The results of a large number of such experiments

have been averaged and are given in the following table:

TABLE XI. — ENERGY USED BY AVERAGE-SIZED MEN (154 POUNDS) PER HOUR UNDER DIFFERENT CONDITIONS OF ACTIVITY; APPROXIMATE AVERAGES ONLY (Copied from Sherman's *Chemistry of Food and Nutrition*, Revised Edition)

Sleeping quietly	60 to 70	Calories
Awake, lying still	77	Calories
Sitting at rest	100	Calories
Standing at rest	115	Calories
Tailoring	135	Calories
Typewriting rapidly	140	Calories
"Light exercise" (stationary bicycle)	170	Calories
Shoemaking	180	Calories
Walking slowly (about $2\frac{3}{4}$ miles per hour)	200	Calories
Carpentry or Metal Work	240	Calories
"Active exercise" (stationary bicycle)	290	Calories
Walking briskly (about $3\frac{3}{4}$ miles an hour)	300	Calories
Stoneworking	400	Calories
Severe exercise, such as sawing wood	450 to 480	Calories
Running (about $5\frac{1}{4}$ miles an hour)	570	Calories
"Very severe exercise" (stationary bicycle)	600	Calories

Sleeping quietly means that the only outward sign of motion is the breathing of the subject. If a person tosses about, he increases the energy used in proportion to the vigor of the motion.

Sitting at rest means reading, sitting at meals, or sitting in a classroom. Much wriggling about in one's seat increases the heat produced, the energy used, and the food required.

Light exercise corresponds to light housework, laboratory work, or running a sewing machine. Students, bookkeepers, stenographers, clerks, and teachers are in this class.

Active exercise corresponds to exercise in the gymnasium, light athletics, like tennis or basketball, house-work, like washing, scrubbing, and sweeping. Athletic girls, general houseworkers, and carpenters are in this class.

Severe muscular exercise includes rapid swimming, fast running, baseball, football, or working with a pick and shovel. This class includes boys and girls engaged in athletics.

Very severe exercise applies chiefly to lumbermen, miners, and men who load and unload freight by hand.

Since the energy requirement of the body may be estimated in Calories, and since the fuel value of foods may be expressed in Calories, we have in the Calorie a common measure both for the needs of the body and for the foods supplying those needs. We frequently speak of the energy requirement in terms of the food value, meaning the number of Calories that the food must supply to provide the energy needed.

To find the Calories needed by an individual weighing 154 pounds and doing a certain kind of work, take for example a man teaching in a high school who walks to and from the building both morning and afternoon and works in his garden part of the day. His energy or food requirement is as follows:

Sleeping — 8 hours	8 × 65	— 520 Calories
Sitting at meals — 2 hours	2 × 100	— 200 Calories
Sitting in the classroom — 4 hours	4 × 100	— 400 Calories
Walking leisurely about the classroom — 3 hours	3 × 170	— 510 Calories
Walking briskly to and from school — 1 hour	1 × 290	— 290 Calories
Working in the garden — 2 hours	2 × 290	— 580 Calories
Reading at night — 3 hours	3 × 100	— 300 Calories
Dressing, bathing, etc., — 1 hour	1 × 170	— 170 Calories
	Total	2970 Calories

Energy requirement varies with size. If the requirement for a man weighing 154 pounds and doing the above-mentioned type of work is 2970 Calories, then a man weighing 129 pounds and doing the same kind of work would require one sixth less food or 2488 Calories. It is sufficiently accurate for all practical purposes to consider the requirements of these two men as 3000 and 2500 Calories respectively.

Since it is easier to calculate the food requirement of one individual without referring to that of another, the following table showing the Calories needed per pound per hour may be more convenient. The Calories needed by any adult may be calculated from it directly without referring to the 154-pound man. (Remember that these figures are for adults only; children require a larger number of Calories per pound. Estimates for children in Calories per day and per pound per day are given in Tables XIII and XIV.)

TABLE XII — AVERAGE CALORIE REQUIREMENT PER POUND PER HOUR FOR ADULTS (Taken from Rose's *Laboratory Handbook for Dietetics*)

Sleeping	0.43 Calories
Sitting at rest	0.65 Calories
Light muscular exercise	1.10 Calories
Active muscular exercise	1.88 Calories
Severe muscular exercise	2.92 Calories

Difference in energy requirements of men and women. There is very little difference in the requirements of men and women of the same age and weight and doing the same kind of work. The average weight of women, however, has been found to be about 20 per cent less than that of men of the same age, so that a

woman's requirement is ordinarily spoken of as 0.8 of
that of man.

To find the energy requirement of a woman let us
take for example a young woman weighing 125 pounds
whose occupation is stenography. She walks to and
from work, plays tennis or takes some other form of
exercise at night, and helps with the housework. Her
food should supply the following number of Calories to
provide for her energy requirement:

Sleeping — 8 hours	(125 × 0.43 × 8) — 430 Calories
Sitting at meals — 2 hours	
Sitting in the office — 7 hours	(125 × 0.65 × 10) — 813 Calories
Reading, etc., at night — 1 hour	
Walking leisurely about the office — 1 hour	
Dressing, etc., — 1 hour	(125 × 1.10 × 4) — 550 Calories
Helping with the housework — 2 hours	
Active walking — 1 hour	(125 × 1.88 × 2) — 470 Calories
Active exercise — 1 hour	

Total 2263 Calories

Lusk of Cornell in summarizing the work of some
Finnish investigators gives the following requirements
for women doing various kinds of work:

A steamstress sewing with a needle	1800 Calories
Seamstresses using a sewing machine	1900–2100 Calories
Bookbinders	1900–2100 Calories
Cleaners of windows and metals	2300–2900 Calories
Washerwomen	2600–3400 Calories

Tigerstedt gives estimates of food requirements for
different degrees of activity as follows:

Shoemaker	2000–2400 Calories
Weaver	2400–2700 Calories
Carpenter or mason	2700–3200 Calories
Farm laborer	3200–4100 Calories
Man digging ditches (excavator)	4100–5000 Calories
Lumberman	Over 5000 Calories

PROBLEMS

17. To find the food requirement of a salesman weighing 150 pounds:

    Yesterday Mr. Jones, a salesman weighing 150 pounds, spent 2 hours at his meals; he spent 1 hour walking to and from the car line; and he spent 2 hours on the car. He worked 8 hours behind the counter selling dry goods, spent 2 hours at the theater, and sat 1 hour reading. He slept 8 hours out of the 24 hours. Calculate the food requirement of Mr. Jones.

18. To find the food requirement of a miner weighing 164 pounds:

    If a miner weighing 164 pounds sleeps 10 hours, works in the mines 8 hours, sits at his meals 2 hours, walks 2 hours, and rests and reads 2 hours, what is his food requirement?

19. To find the food requirement of an adult member of your family:

    (a) Calculate the food requirement of your father or mother. Record the results in your notebook.

    (b) Compare the food requirements of the fathers and mothers of the various members of the class. Account for variations.

Growth influences food requirement. We have been considering the amount of food required by an adult under normal conditions. In determining the needs of any given family where there are growing children and elderly people additional factors must be considered.

If the energy in the food eaten by a child were all used in running about or playing, the child could never grow. He must have food enough to provide for both his play and his growth. For this reason the amount of food needed by a growing boy or girl cannot be reckoned on the same basis as that for an adult. To calculate the requirement of a girl weighing 50 pounds as one third of that of a man weighing 150 pounds would give an insufficient allowance and result in an undernourished child.

The food of the child must be adequate to support a constant increase in weight in addition to providing energy for both internal and external activity.   In the same way in which the food requirement of adults has been determined, an allowance for the boy and the girl of each age has been made as follows:

TABLE XIII. — FOOD ALLOWANCES FOR CHILDREN (Taken from *Food Allowances for Healthy Children*, Pub. 120, A. I. C. P., N. Y.)

AGE — YEARS	CALORIES PER DAY		AGE — YEARS	CALORIES PER DAY	
	Boys	Girls		Boys	Girls
Under 2	900–1200	900–1200	9–10	1700–2000	1550–1850
2–3	1000–1300	980–1280	10–11	1900–2200	1650–1950
3–4	1100–1400	1060–1360	11–12	2100–2400	1750–2050
4–5	1200–1500	1140–1440	12–13	2300–2700	1850–2150
5–6	1300–1600	1220–1520	13–14	2500–2900	1950–2250
6–7	1400–1700	1300–1600	14–15	2600–3100	2050–2350
7–8	1500–1800	1380–1680	15–16	2700–3300	2150–2450
8–9	1600–1900	1460–1760	16–17	2800–4000	2250–2600

The range of from 300 to 700 Calories per day for a child allows for differences in the size and activity of boys and girls of the same age.   "If a child is tall and growing rapidly at six years of age, he may, and probably will, require 1600 Calories.   If of smaller frame, an allowance of only 1400 to 1500 Calories will be necessary with a normal amount of activity.   If he is both large for his age and very active, he will doubtless require the upper limit of the allowance of 1700 Calories," or sometimes even more. Children who are below average weight because they have not been properly fed will require a more liberal allowance than normal children either of the same age or of the same weight. A liberal allowance should be made for underweight children.

The boy playing football or the girl playing basketball requires more food than the boy or girl of the same weight who prefers to sit quietly in the house studying or reading. This, however, should not be used as an argument against vigorous exercise in moderate amounts. There is no doubt that exercise is necessary for the best development. It helps to stimulate growth by creating a hearty appetite which makes the eating of foods containing growth material easier; by increasing respiration, which increases the amount of oxygen inhaled; and by quickening the circulation of the blood, which helps to carry the digested food material to the tissues and to carry waste products out of the system. Food should be sufficient for growth and exercise; otherwise growth is interfered with.

Table XIII applies to the boy or girl of average weight, but there are some children who are very much under or over the average weight for their age. In such instances it is sometimes better to calculate the food requirement according to the weight rather than the age, though every child should have his needs satisfied regardless of the average for either his age or his weight. Generally, when the results of calculating according to age and to weight differ, it is safer to allow the larger of the two estimates. The following table gives the number of Calories usually required per pound per day during the growing period:

TABLE XIV. — CALORIES REQUIRED FOR EACH POUND OF BODY
WEIGHT PER DAY DURING EACH YEAR OF THE GROWING PERIOD
(Compiled from data in Rose's *Feeding the Family*)

Under 1 year	40 to 45 Calories
During the second year	40 to 43 Calories
During the third year	37 to 40 Calories
During the fourth year	37 to 40 Calories
During the fifth year	35 to 37 Calories
During the sixth year	34 to 35 Calories
During the seventh year	32 to 34 Calories
During the eighth year	30 to 35 Calories
During the ninth year	30 to 35 Calories
During the tenth year	28 to 32 Calories
During the eleventh year	28 to 32 Calories
During the twelfth year	28 to 32 Calories
During the thirteenth year	25 to 30 Calories
During the fourteenth year	20 to 25 Calories
During the fifteenth year	20 to 25 Calories
During the sixteenth year	20 to 25 Calories
From the seventeenth year on [1]	
	From 18 Calories up, according to activity

[1] Boys and girls of 17 years and over will need at least as much food as
equally active men and women.

PROBLEMS

20. To find your own Calorie requirement:
    Calculate your own Calorie requirement according to
    figures in Table XIV. If you are above the average weight
    for your height and age, use the higher figure in the range;
    if below the average, use the lower figure. For average
    weight use a figure half way between the higher and lower
    figures as given in Table XIV.

21. Find the Calorie requirement of your young brothers and sisters.
    Consult Tables XIII and XIV. Record the results in your
    notebook.

22. Assemble the Calorie requirements for your entire family.
    Record the results in your notebook.

Energy requirement after middle age. As a man or
woman advances in age, the heart beats more slowly, the

breathing is less rapid, and the internal activities in general become somewhat slower, so that the food needed or energy used to keep up these processes is gradually lessened, until by the eightieth year the food requirement is from one fifth to one third less than during the more active period of life. A woman of eighty needs not more than 2200 Calories where she may have needed 3000 Calories fifty years earlier. The body cannot use as much food as previously and if a person still eats as much as he did during the more active years, there is danger of overtaxing the heart, the kidneys, the liver, and the digestive organs. This in turn may bring about disease directly, or it may weaken the whole system, making it more susceptible to disease or less able to overcome disease that may be brought about through accident. In old age, an extra amount of food eaten over and above the amount actually needed is contrary to the laws of health.

The following table has been suggested by Von Norden as a guide in calculating the food requirements of people sixty years of age and over:

TABLE XV. — TO MODIFY THE FOOD REQUIREMENTS OF ADULTS AFTER MIDDLE AGE

Reduce the normal adult requirement as follows:

For people from 60–70 years of age make a reduction of 10 per cent
For people from 70–80 years of age make a reduction of 20 per cent
For people from 80–90 years of age make a reduction of 30 per cent

PROBLEMS

23. To find the food value of a lunch that has been packed to eat at school:

   (Each girl should be asked in advance to bring a box luncheon to be examined in class.)

Open several lunches that have been brought to school and determine the fuel value of each luncheon, estimating it in terms of 100-Calorie portions.

24. To plan by means of 100-Calorie portions the food for one day for a girl of fifteen:

(a) Plan the breakfast in which the Calories shall be from one fourth to three tenths of the day's supply. Does the breakfast seem sufficient?

(b) For this same girl, plan a dinner that will provide from two fifths to one half of the day's supply of energy.

(c) Complete the day's meals with a supper that will contain the rest of the Calories needed for the day.

25. Calculate the cost of these three meals. Figure the cost per 100 Calories.

Does mental work increase food requirement?   All experiments seem to show that mental work does not increase the food requirement. This may not seem to agree with the experiences of most high-school girls and boys, each of whom will doubtless be ready to testify that he or she is more tired after two or three hours of hard study and steady concentration on some difficult Latin translation or geometry problem than after two or three hours of tennis or football. As a matter of fact, these students doubtless are more conscious of a feeling of exhaustion as the result of study than from the exercise. This may be due to "poisons" produced during nervous tension that settle in the tissues because of lack of exercise and so bring about a feeling of fatigue.

It is advisable to do both mental and muscular work in as calm a frame of mind as possible, reserving tense effort for real emergencies. Fatigue products, if too frequently produced, will cause injury to the body, perhaps by lowering resistance. Any person, experiencing a feeling of exhaustion after concentrated mental work, should exercise virogously to start circulation so that the fatigue products may be carried away from the tissues and eventually be disposed of.

The relation of clothing to the amount of food needed. How can clothing have any effect on the amount of food required? As has been stated previously, heat is produced in the body in proportion to the energy used. By means of a self-regulating system only enough of this heat remains in the body to keep it at uniform temperature. Any excess is given off chiefly through the skin by means of perspiration, and through the lungs in moisture exhaled.

In the summer we are seldom concerned about conserving any of this excess heat, but in winter it is a necessity. Nature helps to conserve the heat on very cold days by causing the blood vessels near the surface to contract under the influence of cold, thus preventing the warm blood from coming to the surface where it would give up its heat to the outside air. This provision of nature is not sufficient protection in cold weather, and if we are wise we wear warm clothing to keep the outside air from absorbing heat; but if the clothing is not warm enough to prevent heat from escaping, the surface is chilled, the nerves in the skin telegraph to the muscles that more heat is needed, and the muscles begin to work to produce heat. If the work which the muscles do for the sole purpose of producing heat is vigorous enough to be apparent it is called shivering, but, however slight it may be, it makes the body do extra work, for which extra food is needed. This extra energy is produced either from food just eaten, or from a reserve source of energy in the tissues, or from the tissues themselves.

A reserve supply will protect the tissues so long as the reserve lasts. If there is no reserve, then the tissues will be burned to produce the energy, and this is dangerous to health. For if this reserve is not replaced there is first a loss of weight, then easy fatigue, lowered resistance, decreased physical ability, and a greater susceptibility to disease, especially tuberculosis.

This scanty clothing is particularly dangerous when the fashion for a slender figure prevails, because heat must be produced in the body to replace that lost through exposure of the skin to the cold air; if there is very little or no adipose tissue to serve as fuel, the muscles will be burned, and with the burning of muscles comes a loss of strength, greater likelihood of illness, and a decrease in the power of the tissues to fight disease germs once they obtain a foothold in the system. Good judgment will prevent the wearing of too thin clothing in cold weather.

QUESTIONS

1. When the body is compared to a delicate machine, and boys and girls to engineers, what are some of the responsibilities of the engineers?

2. The body has the power to store extra fuel. Explain the advantages of this power.

3. Upon what do the energy needs of the body depend? How are these energy needs measured?

4. Explain why (and in what sense) children need more food than adults?

5. How does old age affect a person's food requirement?

6. Does studying increase food requirement? Is it better to eat after studying hard or to take a walk first? Explain.

7. How does the amount of clothing worn in cold weather affect the food requirement? Explain why a reserve supply of tissue is beneficial to health.

8. Completion test:

   An adult sitting at rest needs —— Calories per pound per hour.

   A girl fifteen years of age, normal weight, needs daily —— Calories for each pound of body weight.

   A man needs —— Calories per pound while playing tennis.

   A woman doing light housework uses—— Calories per pound.

REFERENCES

For students:

   ROSE, MARY S. *Feeding the Family*, third edition, Chapter I, pages 11 to 14; Chapter III, pages 50 to 53; Chapter IV, pages 90 to 92. The Macmillan Company (1929).

For teachers:

   ROSE, MARY S. *Foundations of Nutrition*, Chapters IV and V. The Macmillan Company (1927).

   SHERMAN, H. C. *Chemistry of Food and Nutrition*, third edition, Chapters VI and VII. The Macmillan Company (1926).

CHAPTER IV

THE COMPOSITION OF FOODS

FATS, CARBOHYDRATES, AND PROTEINS

FOODS are composed of fats, carbohydrates, proteins, mineral elements, vitamins, and water. Fats and carbohydrates are the chief sources of energy; protein, mineral elements, and vitamins are fundamental in growth and repair of tissues; mineral elements and vitamins stimulate and regulate all life processes; and water is essential for the functioning of all foodstuffs and for all internal activities. A knowledge of the composition of foods and of the needs of the body is fundamental in nutrition and dietetics.

Although the lion's share of all food eaten is burned to produce energy, the person who chooses his food for its energy alone is like the man or woman who chooses a house with a huge furnace regardless of the strength of the walls of the house that help to keep out the cold, or of the number of windows that let in air and sunshine. Just as it is unwise to judge all the qualities of a house by a single, very desirable one, so it is unwise to assume that the remaining requirements of the body will be supplied by food providing sufficient energy. There is only one way in which we may be sure that all the needs of the body will be provided in adequate amounts, and that is by knowing about foods, body needs, and the relationships between them.

61

Food groups.   In any previous work, you have doubt-less been taught to think of foods in groups like, or similar to, the following:

Group   I   Milk
Group II   Meat, fish, poultry, eggs, dry beans, and dry peas
Group III   Vegetables and fruits
Group IV   Bread, cereal, and other grain products
Group   V   Sugars and fats

These food groups are still fundamental and indispensable in planning meals, and they will be referred to later in the discussion of family dietary problems; but suggestions based on these food groups can be stated only in general terms.   To adapt such plans to meet the varying needs of men, women, and children, according to age, weight, and activity, it will be necessary to know what each group and each food in each group contributes to the diet.   Such information will make food selection a more intelligent process and admit of greater variations to meet personal tastes and needs.

Composition of foods. The food chemist tells us that foods are made of carbohydrates (sugars, starches, glycogen, and cellulose), fats, proteins, mineral elements, vitamins, and water.   These substances are called foodstuffs.

Carbohydrates are composed of carbon, hydrogen, and oxygen.
Fats are composed of carbon, hydrogen, and oxygen.
Proteins are composed of carbon, hydrogen, oxygen, nitrogen, sulphur, and sometimes iron and phosphorus.

The mineral elements in foods that are also needed by the body are calcium, chlorine, fluorine, iodine, iron, magnesium, manganese, phosphorus, potassium, silicon, sodium, sulphur, and perhaps copper, and zinc.

Water is composed of hydrogen and oxygen.

MAKING THE FOODSTUFFS READY FOR USE IN THE BODY

The various foodstuffs are broken up in the digestion of food, taken into the blood stream, carried throughout the body as the blood circulates through the arteries and other blood vessels, and are assimilated by the body cells to form and repair muscles, bones, teeth, and all other tissues.

Digestion of food. The first process in the preparation of food for its use in the body is digestion. For good digestion, good teeth and a happy frame of mind are important. The army, recognizing the value of teeth as a factor in preserving the health of its men, requires that every soldier have his teeth in good condition. As we shall see later, food during the early years has a very direct relation to the tendency of teeth to decay. Bad teeth may be responsible for poor health, not only because their owner cannot chew his food properly, but because of the bacteria that lodge and multiply in the cavities and form poisonous products which will be absorbed into the system. Sound, clean teeth are among the most important safeguards of the stomach and of the whole body.

Chewing food prepares the way for quick digestion by separating it into small pieces and by stimulating the flow of the digestive juice in the stomach. Bolting food is not only bad manners; it is injurious to health as well. It adds to the work of the stomach and prolongs the length of time food must remain in the stomach. This increases the danger of fermentation and the production of injurious substances.

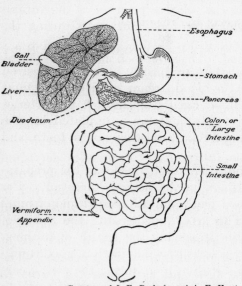

Pleasant anticipation of food stimulates the flow of the digestive juices, while worry and anger retard it. Becoming angry over, or displeased with, food placed before one, or worrying over examinations or lessons poorly prepared, may interfere with digestion so seriously as to cause indigestion.

Courtesy of J. E. Peabody and A. E. Hunt

Illustration No. 3. — A picture of a part of the digestive tract

This shows the relative position of the various organs through which the food must pass during the process of digestion.

Work, well-done, should help to bring about cheerful conversation so that the mealtime may be a joyous occasion.

In the mouth the food should be thoroughly chewed, mixed, and moistened with saliva. This enables the food to pass down into the stomach easily. In the stomach and intestines the food is churned and mixed with the particular digestive juice peculiar to each of these organs until finally it is in a soluble state, ready for absorption. Illustration No. 3 represents the digestive tract, showing the relative position of the various organs through which the food must pass during the process of digestion.

Absorption of food. Digested food, in a soluble state, is absorbed chiefly through the intestinal wall, taken by the blood to all parts of the body, and built up into tissues. As the blood with the digested products flows through the body, each part selects the material it needs to build bones, muscles, and other tissues, or stores it for some future use. Protein is deposited wherever there is need for growth or for repair work; some of the calcium and phosphorus is deposited in bones and teeth; the remainder of the calcium and phosphorus and of all other mineral elements and vitamins helps to form tissues or circulates in the fluids of the body to regulate and stimulate life processes. The major part of the fats and carbohydrates burns to produce energy for the work of the day; the remainder not thus utilized is stored as a packing around nerves, vital organs, and between the muscles and the skin (as subcutaneous fat). In any case, it serves as a reserve supply of fatty tissue (fuel) to be used in time of emergency.

In this way growth takes place, the body is kept in repair, and a reserve is set aside to provide for an emergency. After growth has ceased, there is still need of these digested products in the repairing of the tissues that are constantly wearing out.

Excretion of waste. The worn-out parts are carried away in the blood to be eliminated through the skin, the lungs, the kidneys, and the intestines. It is of vital importance that this material be disposed of before it accumulates to such an extent as to produce poisoning. Headaches, a muddy complexion, and a dull, stupid feeling with no apparent cause may all be the result of improper elimination of these substances.

Normally exercise, plenty of water, and the right kind of food will keep the system flushed and free from this waste material. Since much of it is disposed of through the intestines, great care is necessary to prevent constipation. The bowels should always move at least once a day, while two or three movements a day at regular times are sometimes better.

Interrelationships. The work of the various foodstuffs is a complicated process in which each is valuable only as it coöperates with the others. Although protein is the chief constituent of muscle, protein alone cannot produce growth; mineral elements and vitamins also are necessary for muscle formation. Protein must be accompanied by fats and carbohydrates or it will be used for energy instead of for growth and the maintenance of strength. In the same way, each foodstuff is most useful only in connection with its fellow workers. In general the various foodstuffs are used primarily as follows:

For the production of energy
{
Fats
Carbohydrates
Protein in case of insufficient
  fats and carbohydrates
Vitamins and water as aids

For the growth of new tissues, for the repair of those already grown, and for strength

$\left\{\begin{array}{l}\text{Protein} \\ \text{Mineral elements} \\ \text{Vitamins} \\ \text{Water} \\ \text{Fats and carbohydrates to some extent}\end{array}\right.$

For stimulating and regulating

$\left\{\begin{array}{l}\text{Mineral elements} \\ \text{Vitamins} \\ \text{Water}\end{array}\right.$

Nutrition. To make it possible to select foods which will, under normal conditions, do the things we have claimed for them, it will be necessary to study the kind, the amount, and the use of the foodstuffs in each food; to understand their interrelationships; and to know the amount of each required by individuals under varying conditions, and the combinations most desirable for health. These various phases of the relation of food to growth, health, and activity, together with "factors other than food which influence nutrition," form the basis for the study of nutrition.

FATS AND CARBOHYDRATES

Sugars, starches, and fats are the chief sources of energy. (One gram of fat yields 9 calories, while one gram of sugar or starch yields 4 calories.) Any amount of these foods not used for the production of energy will be stored in the body in the form of adipose tissue. A moderate amount of fat is desirable for appearance and necessary for the support and protection of other tissues, such as nerves and the vital organs. It is also valuable in case of an emergency when more energy is required in one day than the day's supply of food can provide. For instance, the two girls referred to in

Chapter III had eaten an insufficient amount of breakfast to furnish fuel for their unexpected walk of five miles, and the energy required had to be drawn from their tissues. The girl who became tired easily, possessed very little fatty tissue, so that she had to obtain her energy from her muscles.

But, while fats and carbohydrates should occupy a prominent place in a normal, properly balanced diet, it is neither necessary nor desirable to have a very large surplus of fatty tissue. Too much fat means an extra burden for heart and other organs, which results in discomfort, inefficiency, and waste of energy. One has only to watch the very fat man or woman hurrying to catch a passing car or struggling up a flight of stairs, to realize one of the disadvantages of adipose tissue and the work involved in carrying it about.

Then, too, foods containing the most concentrated forms of sweets as well as fats, do not in general contain much else in the way of nourishment; and if too large a proportion of the energy is derived from these foods, there is danger that an insufficient quantity of other foodstuffs will be taken.

Carbohydrates. Carbohydrates are manufactured in the chlorophyll cells of green leaves. The leaves absorb carbon dioxide (CO_2) from the air, and the roots absorb water (H_2O) from the soil. In some way the sun's rays acting on the green leaves cause carbon, hydrogen, and oxygen to unite, and form such compounds as sugars, starches, and other carbohydrates.

Carbohydrates commonly found in foods are sugars, starches, glycogen, and cellulose; dextrin, although not found in uncooked food, is formed in some cooking processes and during the digestion of starch and plays a part in nutrition. Carbohydrates are found chiefly in foods of vegetable origin, such as grains, vegetables, and fruits; in addition to being found in foods of vegetable origin, sugar is found in milk, and glycogen is found in oysters, liver, and a few other tissues. With few exceptions, the foods richest in fats have very little carbohydrate, while those with a large amount of

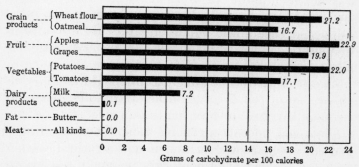

Chart VIII. — A comparison of some common foods on the basis of the number of grams of carbohydrate per 100 Calories

carbohydrate contain very little fat. This relationship is brought out more clearly in Chart VIII, in which the comparative richness in carbohydrates of various types of foods is represented.

Sugars. Milk contains one of the most easily digested carbohydrates in the form of lactose or milk sugar. This sugar, with the fat in milk, provides energy for the infant during the first year of life, before he is able to take much else in the way of nourishment. It dissolves slowly, does not ferment readily, and is unlikely to cause fermentation or irritation.

Cane sugar, maple sugar, maple syrup, molasses, corn syrup, and honey are ordinarily considered as the important sources of sugar for older children and adults; but there is also a valuable supply in dates, raisins, and prunes among fruits, and in beets, green peas, carrots, sweet corn, sweet potatoes, and squash among vegetables. These foods are sometimes called nature's sugar bowls, because they are examples of the harmless way in which nature provides her sugar for us. Sugars are soluble in water and hence cannot be seen in moist fruits and vegetables, but when fruits are dried, sugar frequently appears in small lumps, especially in raisins.

Sugars, with the possible exception of lactose, yield energy more rapidly than other foodstuffs; they are absorbed quickly and give immediate relief from fatigue, but, because of this quick reaction, their use is often abused. When sugar is taken in too large amounts there is danger of fermentation before it can be absorbed; thus the way is paved to irritation of the mucous membrane of stomach and intestines, and, later, to chronic digestive trouble. Sugar itself, in concentrated form, is also irritating to the stomach; in addition, it tends to make other foods containing mineral elements and vitamins seem less attractive. Since the use of much sugar may upset digestion and destroy a desire for the more essential foods, it is well to limit the amount to not more than two or three tablespoonfuls a day. Sugar should be taken in dilute form, as in cocoa, on cooked fruit, and in simple desserts. The place for concentrated sweets (if any) is at the end of a meal; never early in a meal, or between two meals.

Starches. The chief sources of starch are cereals, flour, cornmeal, macaroni, and other foods made from wheat, oats, rye, rice, barley, corn, or other grain products. Of the vegetables, corn, potatoes (both white and sweet), dry beans, dry peas, and lentils are richest in starch. Ripe fruit (with the exception of bananas) and animal products, such as eggs, milk, and meat, with the exception of the tissues containing glycogen, contain no starch.

Starch is the largest single source of energy after the first year of life. During digestion it is changed to sugar by the digestive juices. Because starch goes through this extra process, it is digested and absorbed much more slowly than sugar, and hence is less likely to cause fermentation and irritation; for this reason it is the safer source of energy. After the second year, about one third of the energy of children should come from bread, cereals, potatoes, and other common starchy foods.

Dextrin. Dextrin is an intermediate product formed as starch is changed to sugar under the influence of the digestive juices; it may be formed also from starch under the influence of inorganic acids or by long heating. The brown crust formed during the baking or toasting of bread is dextrinized starch. As this dextrinized starch is partly soluble, bread thoroughly dried in the oven or toasted is more easily digested than fresh, moist bread.

Glycogen. Glycogen, frequently called animal starch, is found in oysters, scallops, lobsters, and sometimes in liver and kidney; it is present also in living muscle tissue. Glycogen is the form in which digested starch and sugar are stored in the liver and muscles and from which energy is produced as needed. These storehouses of energy help to keep the blood sugar at a normal level and thus to prevent harm from an overabundance of sugar in the tissues. Glycogen accumulates in the liver during rest, but during vigorous exercise it may be exhausted completely; it is at this point that fatty tissue is called upon for energy.

Cellulose. Cellulose is the fibrous material which holds the other foodstuffs in grain products, vegetables, and fruits in position. So far as we know, it is not digested in the human digestive tract to any great extent. Therefore it can be used neither for fuel nor for growth, yet it plays a very important part in health. It gives bulk to the food in the intestines and helps to prevent constipation by stimulating the elimination of waste.

PROBLEM

26. To separate the cellulose and starch in potato:

   Grate a small potato. Put the grated material into a piece of cheese cloth and wash the mass thoroughly in a bowl of cold water. The bulky, fibrous material remaining in the cloth is cellulose. Test with iodine the white material that settles to the bottom of the bowl for starch. Remove the fibrous material and dry it. Examine it the next day. Cellulose and starch with water form the bulk of the materials in vegetables and fruits.

Fats. Fat is formed in both plant and animal life. Animals make their adipose tissue from both fats and carbohydrates which are taken in as food, but it is probable that plants form the fat in their tissues from carbohydrates alone. Fat is composed of carbon, hydrogen, and oxygen, as are the carbohydrates, but in proportion to the other two elements it contains less oxygen than do the carbohydrates. It therefore requires more oxygen for combustion which results in the production of energy. The greater the amount of oxygen used in the burning of a food, the more heat produced and the richer the food becomes as a source of energy. Because fat requires such a large amount of oxygen for its oxidation, it is a very concentrated source of energy.

Although fat is the most concentrated form of fuel, it is not always the best form for all people. It is digested more slowly than starch, and it may retard the digestion of other foods. Retarded digestion often causes discomfort from gas formed, while continued indigestion may eventually cause an irritation of the lining of the digestive tract. On the other hand, because fat leaves the stomach slowly it will be beneficial for those who digest food rapidly and feel hungry soon after a hearty meal. Those who exercise vigorously in the open air have less difficulty in the digestion of fat than those leading an indoor life. Fat cooked at a high temperature, as in frying, is irritating to the mucous membrane of stomach and intestines; this makes fried foods especially objectionable for children, invalids, and those with weak digestion.

Source of fats and oils. It is needless to mention the more common foods valuable for fat, as butter, lard, fat meat, oil, and cream; but perhaps it is not so generally known that when we eat cheese, milk, eggs, oatmeal, olives, and nuts we obtain considerable fat from them. Table XVI gives the number of grams of fat in 100-Calorie portions of the various foods.

TABLE XVI. — GRAMS OF FAT AND CARBOHYDRATE IN THE 100-CALORIE PORTION OF EACH OF SEVERAL COMMON FOODS (Arranged from Rose's *Laboratory Manual of Dietetics*)

SUGARS AND GRAIN PRODUCTS

	Grams of Fat	Grams of Carbohydrate
Sugars		
Honey		24.9
Maple syrup		25.0
Molasses		24.2
Sugar		25.0
Grain Products		
Barley	0.3	21.8
Bread (avg.)	0.5	20.4
Cornmeal	0.5	21.2
Farina	0.4	21.1
Flour (avg.)	0.4	21.2
Hominy	0.2	22.3
Macaroni	0.3	20.7
Oatmeal	1.8	16.7
Rice	0.1	22.5
Shredded wheat	0.5	20.6

FRUITS

	Grams of Fat	Grams of Carbohydrate
Apples	0.6	22.9
Apricots	0.4	22.5
Bananas	0.6	22.3
Blackberries	1.7	18.9
Blueberries	1.0	21.7
Cantaloupes		23.5
Cherries	1.1	21.4
Currants	0.5	23.1
Dates	0.8	22.6
Figs	0.1	23.4
Grapes	1.7	19.9
Lemons	1.6	19.1
Olives	9.2	3.9
Oranges	0.3	22.8
Peaches	0.3	22.9
Pears	0.7	22.5
Pineapples		22.5
Plums		23.9
Prunes		24.3
Raisins	1.0	22.1
Raspberries	1.5	19.1
Strawberries	1.6	18.9
Watermelons	0.8	21.6

VEGETABLES

	Grams of Fat	Grams of Carbohydrate
Asparagus	0.9	14.9
Beans, white	0.5	17.3
Beans, Lima	0.4	18.9
Beans, string	0.9	17.8
Beets	0.3	20.9
Cabbage	0.8	18.1
Carrots	0.6	21.1
Cauliflower	1.6	15.4
Celery	0.7	17.5
Chard	1.6	13.1
Corn	1.2	19.4
Cucumbers	1.3	17.3
Dandelions	1.6	18.3
Eggplants	1.1	18.3
Kohlrabi	0.3	17.8
Lentils	0.3	17.8
Lettuce	1.3	15.8
Onions	0.7	20.3
Parsnips	0.8	20.1
Peas	0.3	17.4
Peppers, green	0.4	19.2
Potatoes, sweet	0.6	22.0
Potatoes, white	0.2	22.0
Pumpkins	0.8	19.6
Radishes	0.5	19.5
Rhubarb	2.9	15.7
Spinach	1.3	13.4
Squash	0.9	19.9
Tomatoes	1.8	17.1
Turnips	0.4	20.9

MILK, NUTS, FISH, EGGS, CHEESE, MEAT, FATS

	Grams of Fat	Grams of Carbohydrate
Milk		
Con'd, sweet	2.5	16.8
Skimmed	0.8	13.9
Buttermilk	1.4	13.4
Whole	5.8	7.2
Con'd, unsweetened	5.6	6.7
Nuts		
Almonds	8.5	2.7
Coconuts	8.6	4.7
Chestnuts	2.2	17.3
Filberts	9.3	1.8
Peanuts	7.0	4.5
Pecans	9.6	2.1
Walnuts	9.1	1.9
Fish, lean	0.7	
Fish, oily	5.0	
Eggs	7.1	
Cheese (Am.)	8.2	0.1
Meat, lean	5.0	
Meat, fat	11.0	
Fats		
Bacon	10.4	
Butter	11.1	
Cream, 18%	9.5	2.3
Cream, 40%	10.5	0.8
Lard	11.1	
Oils	11.1	
Pork, salt	11.0	

According to average figures, fruits, vegetables, and grain products in general contain less than 1 per cent by weight of fat; oatmeal and olives are the exception to the rule, with 7 and 20 per cent respectively. Lard and oils are 100 per cent fat, while butter has only 85 per cent. From 50 to 60 per cent of most nuts is fat, with the exception of peanuts, which have only 38 per cent, and chestnuts, which have only 5 per cent. If we wish

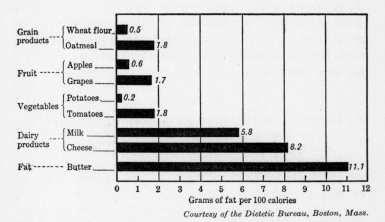

Courtesy of the Dietetic Bureau, Boston, Mass.

Chart IX. — A comparison of some common foods on the basis of the number of grams of fat per 100 Calories

to increase the Calories of the diet without increasing the bulk unduly, then oatmeal, olives, nuts, and cheese, in addition to butter and other easily recognized fatty foods, may be used effectively.

Chart IX shows the comparative richness in fat of the various types of foods. It contains one or two representative foods from the grain products, vegetables, fruits, dairy products, and fats.

Amount of fat. Although the amount of fat in the diet will vary with the ability of the individual to care for it, the minimum allowance estimated as desirable by scientists is between two and three ounces (57 to 85 grams) a day. If boys and girls receive at least this amount in such foods as butter, cream, bacon, fat meat, and oils, additional amounts from other foods will provide a margin of safety without overtaxing the digestive system. Some people can digest and use to good advantage an amount of fat greater than that mentioned, but since fat is likely to retard digestion, each person should use it cautiously and be guided by his own reactions to fatty foods.

PROBLEMS

27. To compare the fat content of various foods:

    How much of each of the following foods does it take to give two ounces (56.7 grams) of fat?

Butter	Milk	Olives	Medium fat beef
Cream	Peanuts	Eggs	Chocolate (milk, sweetened)

28. Plan an 800-Calorie meal containing one ounce of fat. How does this quantity of fat compare with the amount of fat you usually eat at one meal?

29. Arrange a meal for yourself in which one third of the energy will be supplied by cereals, breadstuffs, and potatoes.

30. Prepare and calculate the amount of energy in a pound of fudge. Cut it into pieces, each of which will furnish 100 Calories. To how many pieces should you limit yourself in one day? When is the best time to eat it?

31. To compare the economic value of various foods as sources of energy:

    How much would it cost to obtain one third of the energy you need in one day from each of any five of the following foods?

Lean beef	Eggs	Milk	Dry beans
Butter	Cream (18%)	Potatoes	Olive oil
Bread	Macaroni	Walnuts	Cornmeal

(Calculate the cost of each at current prices.)

PROTEINS

Proteins are found in foods of both animal and vegetable origin.   They and the substances closely related

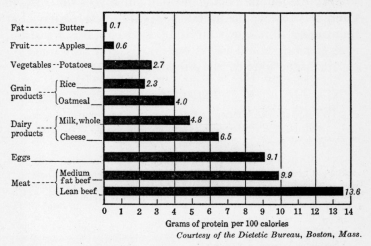

Grams of protein per 100 calories

Courtesy of the Dietetic Bureau, Boston, Mass.

Chart X. — A comparison of some common foods on the basis of the number of grams of protein per 100 Calories

to them are the only organic compounds containing nitrogen with which we have to do in nutrition.   Plants make their own protein from carbon, hydrogen, and oxygen, all of which are absorbed by the leaves, with nitrogen, which is absorbed from the soil through the roots; but animals are unable to form proteins from these simple elements.   Therefore they must have some protein food in their diet from which to construct the kind of protein that will suit their own individual needs.

Where do we find protein? Protein is found naturally in every food that grows; some foods are very rich in it, while some foods have so little that the protein content is almost negligible. Some foods, like white sugar, have had all the protein removed by artificial refining processes. Tables XVII and XVIIA give a general idea of the best sources of protein, while Chart X represents graphically the relative protein content of some common foods.

TABLE XVII. — THE RELATIVE VALUE OF COMMON FOODS FOR PROTEIN (The foods are listed alphabetically)

BEST SOURCES OF PROTEIN	FOODS CONTAINING PRACTICALLY NO PROTEIN
Bread and Cereals [1]	Fats and oils
Cheese	Fruits
Eggs	Rice
Legumes (dry beans, peas, lentils)	Sugar and syrups
Meat	Vegetables, except those given in
Milk	the other column
Nuts	
Potatoes [1]	

[1] When eaten in large amounts.

Use of protein. Years ago people had the impression that protein was chiefly responsible for the strength-giving property of food, because it was found in every living cell. And for a long time scientists thought it was the essential substance of life, but gradually they discovered the value and the interresponsibility of both mineral elements and vitamins in health and vigor. Yet, while no one foodstuff may be said to be more

TABLE XVIIA. — COMMON FOODS GROUPED AND LISTED IN THE ORDER OF THE AMOUNT OF PROTEIN (IN GRAMS) IN THE 100-CALORIE PORTIONS (Arranged from tables in Sherman's *Chemistry of Food and Nutrition*) Keep in mind the size of the 100-Calorie portion of these foods

	VEGETABLES	FRUITS	MEAT, FISH, MILK, EGGS, CHEESE, NUTS	GRAIN PRODUCTS	FATS, SUGARS
Over 10 grams			Fish (lean), clams, veal, oysters, beef (lean)		
5-10 grams	Spinach, chard, asparagus, lentils, Brussels sprouts, peas, kohlrabi, shell beans, lettuce, cauliflower, string beans, cabbage		Milk (skimmed), eggs, pork (lean), fowl, buttermilk, beef (med. fat), lamb, mutton, cheese		
3-5 grams	Cucumbers, peppers (green), radishes, egg plant, tomatoes, dandelions, pumpkin, beets, onions, turnips, corn, squash		Milk, whole, fresh, dried, or condensed (unsweetened), peanuts, pork (fat), cocoa, almonds	Oatmeal, entire wheat bread, entire wheat flour, graham flour, macaroni, shredded wheat, rye bread, white bread, graham bread, white flour, farina	
1-3 grams	Potatoes, rhubarb, parsnips, carrots, celery	Currants (fresh), raspberries, strawberries, blackberries, lemons, apricots, peaches, oranges, cantaloupe, figs, grapes, bananas, watermelon, plums, grapefruit, cherries, pears	Milk, condensed (sweetened), chestnuts, walnuts, hazelnuts, chocolate, pecans, coconut	Boston brown bread, cornmeal, crackers (soda), hominy, rice (white), rye flour, buckwheat flour	Bacon, Cream, 18%
Below 1 gram		Cranberries, pineapple, blueberries, currants (dry), raisins, prunes, apples, dates, olives		Tapioca	Molasses, butter, honey, maple syrup Cream, 40%

important than another, it is true that protein is needed in largest amounts for growth and the maintenance of strength.

Protein is necessary to keep young tissues growing, to keep grown tissues in repair, and to replace those wasted by disease. Growing boys and girls must have protein enough, both in kind and in amount, to help them to become healthy men and women; people who have been ill must have it to help them to recover strength; all need it to keep up vitality. But, for whatever purpose it is eaten, it must be accompanied by a proper amount of other foodstuffs.

Relative value of proteins. Not all proteins are equally valuable. Of two foods containing the same amount of protein but from different sources, one may help children to grow vigorously, while the other may be unable to maintain in good condition tissues already grown. Proteins that will serve for growth, for repair, and for maintaining the strength of a healthy individual are said to be complete proteins. Proteins that will keep healthy adults in good condition but are unable to support growth in children or to help those recovering from illness are called partially complete proteins. Proteins which can neither support growth nor maintain grown tissues in good condition are called incomplete proteins. All proteins found in animal tissues (except gelatin) are complete proteins, while, in general, grains and vegetables contain proteins that are either incomplete or partially complete.

When incomplete or partially complete proteins are combined with complete proteins, they are used for both growth and maintenance. It is conceivable that two foods containing incomplete proteins may supplement each other and do the work of one complete protein; but to make this practicable it would be necessary to know protein values thoroughly. As we do not know how all the various proteins compare with one another in their ability to build and to keep grown tissues in repair, it is safest to include in the diet each day, at least a small amount of protein from some animal source, such as milk, eggs, meat, or fish. With even a little animal protein, the bulk of the protein may be from bread, cereals, and vegetables.

Amino acids. Each protein is made up of a large number of smaller parts called amino acids, some of

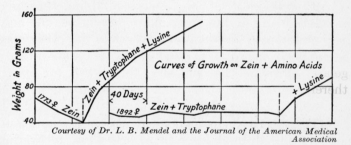

Courtesy of Dr. L. B. Mendel and the Journal of the American Medical Association

Chart XI. — The upward trend of these growth curves shows the favorable influence of tryptophane and lysine

which have such an influence on growth that growth is interfered with when foods containing these particular amino acids are absent. These essential amino acids are trypotophane, lysine, cystine, histidine, tyrosine, and perhaps proline. Chart XI shows how growth was favorably influenced when tryptophane and lysine, two of the essential amino acids, were added to a diet with zein as its only protein. Zein is one of the pro-

teins in corn which contains neither lysine nor tryptophane. Illustration No. 4 shows the difference in
growth between rats fed complete and incomplete
proteins.

Milk proteins have the most perfect combination of
all the various amino acids, as they include each of
those essential for growth. This completeness makes

Courtesy of E. V. McCollum, Ph.D.

Illustration No. 4. — These two rats are of the same age; the rat at the
right-hand side of the picture had a diet containing complete proteins,
while the rat at the left had a diet containing only incomplete, or
partially complete, proteins.

milk one of the best foods for growing boys and girls.
All other proteins of animal origin, with the exception of
gelatin, contain all the essential amino acids and are
therefore examples of complete proteins, capable of
promoting growth and keeping grown tissues in repair.
Gelatin, although of animal origin, is an incomplete
protein. It is, however, valuable both for growth and
for maintenance when supplemented with a small
amount of a complete protein.

Many of the proteins in grains are incomplete or partially complete. The one called gliadin (which occurs in wheat) contains no lysine, and, while it will not help growing boys and girls unless supplemented with a complete protein which contains lysine, it may be used as the only source of protein for adults. It is then a partially complete protein, because it will maintain grown tissues in good condition but will not support growth. If the protein called zein, which occurs in corn, is used as the only source of protein, it will neither support growth nor protect adults unless used with a food containing the amino acid missing in its make-up. (See Chart XI.) For this reason, zein is an example of an incomplete protein. Both wheat and corn contain complete proteins as well as the incomplete, but these are largely removed in the ordinary milling processes, so that refined flour and meal should be supplemented, preferably by milk. Bread made with milk offers a better protein mixture than does bread made with water.

Amount of protein required daily. Much work has been done to determine the amount of protein needed daily. These experiments, made by different people, have given results so similar that it seems safe to assume that the average may be used as a guide in estimating the amount required by any one individual under normal conditions.

The amount stated as adequate to maintain the health and strength of an adult with a liberal margin for safety is 0.5 gram of protein for every pound of body weight,[1] or 70 grams for a person weighing 154 pounds.

[1] See Sherman's *Chemistry of Food and Nutrition*, third edition.

This 0.5 gram does not provide for growth; all growing boys and girls need more protein in proportion to weight than adults. The amount varies from 1.5 to 2 grams per pound of body weight for very young children and gradually decreases with an increase in age to the 0.5 gram for adults.

A more reliable way of satisfying the protein needs of children is to allow about 30 grams of protein for every 1000 Calories; another satisfactory method is to provide from 10 to 15 per cent of the Calories through protein (1 gram of protein yields 4 Calories). If we provide from 10 to 15 per cent of the Calories through protein, we have a protein allowance per Calorie requirement corresponding to the figures given in Table XVIII.

TABLE XVIII. — GRAMS OF PROTEIN FOR GROWING CHILDREN ACCORDING TO CALORIE NEED

CALORIES	GRAMS OF PROTEIN
1000	25 to 38
1200	30 to 45
1400	35 to 53
1600	40 to 60
1800	45 to 68
2000	50 to 75
2200	55 to 83
2400	60 to 90
2600	65 to 98
2800	70 to 105
3000	75 to 113

The amount required will vary with the kind of protein, and may be influenced by the quantity of other foodstuffs. It is considered best to have some protein from an animal source, with an adequate amount of each of the other foodstuffs, such as mineral elements, vitamins, fats, and carbohydrates. The food of an adult should contain only enough protein to meet daily needs, as an excess is not easily stored, but must be digested and excreted by way of the kidneys, possibly causing injury to them.

Contrary to a very common idea, the amount of protein needed will not vary with the kind of work done, provided energy foods are adequate. The studious boy or girl needs as much protein as the one who enters vigorously into athletics, if the two are of the same age and weight. The athlete will require more energy than the student, but not necessarily more protein.

In making any accurate dietary calculations it is necessary to have accurate figures. The exact amount of the number of grams of protein in the 100-Calorie portion of each common food is given in Tables XXII, XXIII, XXIV, XXV, and XXVI.

PROBLEMS

32. Calculate your own protein requirement. How many Calories will this amount of protein furnish? How many Calories must you obtain from fats and carbohydrates to complete your total Calorie requirement? Does your protein supply about 10 to 15 per cent of your total Calories?

33. Calculate the amount of protein needed by each member of your family. Record these amounts in your notebook.

34. If a boy needs three ounces (85 grams) of protein in a day, how much lean beef would be necessary to supply it? How much milk? How much whole wheat bread? What quantity of baked beans? If these four foods are to supply the three ounces of protein the boy needs in one day, how much of each food will be required to form such a combination?

35. Plan a day's supply of protein for yourself. Arrange the actual foods according to the three meals of the day. Explain the relative value of the proteins you have selected.

36. Calculate the amount of different protein-rich foods that your family needs to supply them with a sufficient amount of protein for a day.

QUESTIONS

1. How does the classification of foods in this chapter differ from the food groups you studied in elementary school?

2. Name the foodstuffs and the elements which compose each foodstuff.

3. How are these various foodstuffs made over into your body tissue?

4. How can an individual aid his digestion?

5. In what ways can an individual aid in the elimination of waste products from his body?

6. Explain what is meant by the interrelationships of the different foodstuffs.

7. Sugars and starches are the chief sources of energy. From what foods do you prefer to get your starch? From what foods do you prefer to get your sugar? What other foods containing starch and sugar could you eat to extend your diet?

8. How many Calories does one gram of sugar or starch yield? How many Calories does one gram of fat yield? How many Calories does one gram of protein yield?

9. Fats are two and one quarter times as rich in fuel as starches and sugars. What is the objection to supplying all one's energy with fat? What other uses has fat in the body besides yielding energy?

10. Why is protein such a necessary foodstuff? Can any other foodstuff be substituted for it? Why are some proteins more valuable than others?

11. What influences the amount of protein you need? Why is it unwise to eat large amounts of protein?

12. Completion test:

Cereals, bread, and potatoes should furnish —— —— of the energy for children.

Cellulose furnishes the digestive tract with ——.

Proteins are classified as ——, ——, and ——.

Proteins are made up of smaller parts called —— ——.

REFERENCES

For students:

HARRIS, J. W. and LACEY, E. V. *Everyday Foods*, Unit Four, pages 216 to 226. Houghton Mifflin Company (1927).

ROSE, MARY S. *Feeding the Family*, third edition, Chapter I, pages 15 to 18; Chapter II; Chapter III, pages 79 to 85. The Macmillan Company (1929).

For teachers:

ROSE, MARY S. *Foundations of Nutrition*, Chapter VII, pages 122 to 147; Chapter XI, pages 300 to 304. The Macmillan Company (1927).

ROSE, MARY S. *Laboratory Handbook for Dietetics*, revised edition, Part I. The Macmillan Company (1929).

SHERMAN, H. C. *Chemistry of Food and Nutrition*, third edition, Chapters I, II, III, and IV. The Macmillan Company (1926).

CHAPTER V

MINERAL ELEMENTS

VALUABLE as are proteins, fats, and carbohydrates, these foodstuffs would be useless without mineral elements and vitamins. Mineral elements and vitamins control all the processes which make possible growth, health, and activity. Because of the small amount of each of these regulators in the body, we frequently fail to appreciate the attention required to insure adequate amounts of them. With even the small amount below normal, disaster of one kind or another, is sure to follow. Those that need special thought are calcium, iron, iodine, and vitamins A, B, C, D, and G.

Milk, eggs, fruits, and vegetables, especially green leafy vegetables, are the chief sources of both mineral elements and vitamins; these foods should be used freely by both adults and children.

MINERAL ELEMENTS

What are mineral elements? We are familiar with the residue or ash left from the burning of coal or wood. There is also a small residue or ash left when any food except pure oil, fat, starch, or sugar is burned. This food ash consists of several different substances, each of which is composed of two or more elements from the mineral kingdom. These mineral elements do not exist, in foods and in the body, as simple elements like those we see in the laboratory, but they are combined with other substances to form complex chemical compounds.

Mineral elements will not burn inside the body any more than they will burn outside the body; hence they are not used as fuel. They are held in solution, which admits of their being carried to every part of the body; some of them remain in soluble form, circulating in the fluids to stimulate and regulate the internal processes which keep us alive, while others are deposited in the tissues as solids.

The mineral elements which are known to exist in foods, and which are found also in the body, are calcium, chlorine, fluorine, iodine, iron, magnesium, manganese, phosphorus, potassium, silicon, sodium, and sulphur; others which may be present are aluminum, arsenic, copper, and zinc. Some foods are valuable for one mineral element, some are valuable for another, and some are valuable for several; but very few are equally valuable for them all. Hence it is well to have a variety of foods to make sure that we receive all the mineral elements needed.

Importance of mineral elements. Mineral elements form a large part of the structure of bones and teeth; they also enter into the composition of other tissues, and some of them are dissolved in the blood and tissues, where they help to control and to regulate body processes. They make breathing and digestion possible; they help to maintain steadiness of nerve; they assist in the burning of food to produce energy; they are responsible for the contraction and relaxation of muscles, and for all other activities. Mineral elements keep the blood in good condition; they also preserve the neutrality of blood and tissues by keeping a proper balance between acids and bases (alkalis).

With a low mineral intake there may follow "spring fever," lassitude, headaches, easy fatigue, irritability, nervousness, restlessness, constipation, or other symptoms of a below-par feeling. Many serious illnesses are

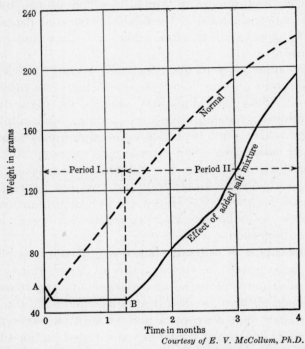

Courtesy of E. V. McCollum, Ph.D.

Chart XII. — Effect upon growth of the addition to a diet otherwise adequate of a salt mixture of such composition as to make the composition of the total ash similar to that of milk

doubtless the result, either directly or indirectly, of a deficiency of mineral elements, but oftentimes such conditions develop too slowly to be associated with the real cause.

Human life would cease without some of each of the mineral elements known to exist in the body, but because of the usual varied diet there is little likelihood of a complete absence of any one of them; the danger arises from an amount below that needed for normal growth and vigorous health. Chart XII shows what happened

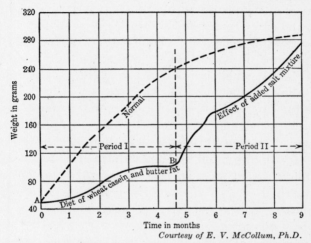

Courtesy of E. V. McCollum, Ph.D.

Chart XIII. — Growth at much less than half the normal rate through the greater part of the normal growth period, followed by accelerated growth upon the addition of a suitable salt mixture to the diet

to rats that were fed on a diet without proper mineral elements. From A to B, as represented on the chart, the rats had too small an amount of certain mineral elements, and no growth took place. At B, mineral elements were added, and the animals grew normally. Chart XIII shows the effect of a similar diet, low in minerals, but good in all other respects. At B, when the mineral content of the diet was made adequate, growth was stimulated and was soon normal. It is quite probable that many boys and girls are below standard development because they are not receiving a proper amount of the various mineral elements.

The acid-base influence of foods. In our daily living, acids and bases (alkalis) are formed in the tissues as the result of chemical processes. These chemical processes produce growth and energy, promote digestion and the circulation of the blood, and underlie all other internal activities. Food eaten will also influence the amount of acid or alkali present in the tissues, for some foods, when burned in the body, produce acids and some produce alkaline substances.

Normally, the alkalis (or bases) in the system counteract the acids, and vice versa, preserving a neutrality which is essential for health and a high degree of resistance to disease; but if either the acids or the bases predominate to such an extent as to cause either a strong acid or a strong alkaline condition, undesirable symptoms appear which may develop into a serious physical condition.

An excess of alkali is less likely to occur than an excess of acid. And if there is insufficient alkali to neutralize the acid formed, the tissues may be injured by the acid. Therefore it is well to have an abundance of base-forming foods in the diet.

Base-forming foods	*Acid-forming foods*
Fruits (except those mentioned under acid-forming foods)	Meat and fish
	Eggs
Vegetables (except corn)	Bread, cereals, macaroni, rice, and other foods made from grains
Milk and cheese	
	Corn (which is really a grain)
	Plums, prunes, and cranberries

Fats, oils, and sugars, when taken in small amounts, are neutral, but a large amount of any one of them will tend to produce acid in the tissues. The fact that rice is acid-forming while potatoes are base-forming is an argument against the frequent substitution of rice for potatoes. In general, it is wise to serve base-forming foods with acid-forming foods, as potatoes with meat; cheese or tomatoes with macaroni; and milk with bread, especially for children.

Although fruit is acid outside the body, the compounds in which its mineral elements are held are easily broken down to form other compounds which are alkaline, so that most fruits form alkaline substances in the body. Cranberries, plums, and prunes are exceptions to this general rule, as they have an acid effect in the system. Some people seem to burn acid fruits less easily than others. But, in general, the eating of fruits, as well as of milk and vegetables, will help to counteract an acid condition in the system.

Certain mineral elements need special attention. Calcium, phosphorus, and iron are the mineral elements most abundantly needed, and it is probable that other mineral elements, with the exception of iodine, will be adequate if proper provisions are made for these three; accordingly calcium, phosphorus, and iron will be discussed in greater detail than the others, and they should be given special attention in the planning of meals.

CALCIUM AND PHOSPHORUS

Calcium and phosphorus make up the bulk of the bones and the teeth and aid in the construction and growth of other tissues. Rickets and carious teeth will occur with too little calcium or phosphorus, or with a deficiency of both (or with insufficient vitamin D, the value of which will be discussed later). Boys and girls, men and women, who have had diets low in calcium and phosphorus during the early years are likely to have lowered resistance and greater suceptibility to pneumonia and other diseases of the respiratory tract.

A

B

Courtesy of the Bureau of Home Economics, U. S. Department of Agriculture, Washington, D. C.

Illustration No. 5. — Influence of calcium on the growth of rats. These two rats are of the same age; rat A had insufficient calcium in an otherwise adequate diet; rat B had adequate calcium in his diet

Calcium. In addition to the formation of bones, teeth, and other tissues, and the building up of a resistance, calcium is necessary for the regulation of nervous, muscular, and glandular control, and for the coagulation of the blood. If a person's food, in any one day, has a low calcium content, it is true that the amount required by the tissues will be drawn from bones and teeth, and no immediate harm may be apparent until the teeth begin to decay.   But if this borrowing process continues for years, the reserve supply in the bones will eventually run low, and a breakdown, for which there seems to be no explanation, is sure to follow.   Illustration No. 5 shows the influence of a low calcium diet.   The rats pictured are of the same age.   The rat on the low calcium diet, in the upper picture has grown very little, and his general appearance is quite inferior to that of the rat on a diet adequate in calcium.

Calcium is needed in larger amounts than any of the other mineral elements; it is more often lacking in our diet than any other foodstuff; and there are few foods that contain it in any considerable amount.   For these reasons the amount of calcium needed, and ways of introducing it into the diet, need careful study.

A safety calcium allowance. Experiments have shown that, for the average man weighing 154 pounds, 0.67 gram of calcium daily, or approximately 0.005 gram per pound of body weight, will cover his daily need and provide a margin of safety.   Activity and sex do not influence the adult calcium requirement, but it varies in proportion to weight.   Then, in determining a safety calcium allowance for men and women weighing less than 154 pounds, multiply the weight of the individual by 0.005.

Because the bones and teeth of children are constantly increasing in size, growing boys and girls need more calcium in proportion to weight than do men and women.   Sherman, who has done much work on the food requirements of children, suggests an allowance of at least one gram of calcium per day during the growing period, regardless of weight or age.

Foods valuable for calcium. Chart XIV represents graphically the relative value of some common foods for calcium; Table XIX gives foods grouped according to relative calcium value; while the amount of calcium in 100-Calorie portions of common foods is given in Tables XXII, XXIII, XXIV, XXV, and XXVI. A study of the chart and the tables will make it clear that

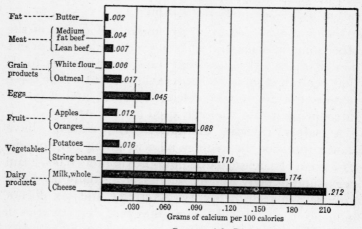

Courtesy of the Dietetic Bureau, Boston, Mass.

Chart XIV. — A comparison of some common foods on the basis of the number of grams of calcium per 100 Calories

milk and cheese are the only foods containing calcium in large enough amounts to insure an adequate supply for the body. Carrots, turnips, parsnips, string beans, cauliflower, celery, and spinach contain a fair amount, but to obtain the day's supply from these foods would require from two to four pounds of any one of them or the same number of pounds from a combination of several. Diets containing these vegetables in such large quanti-

TABLE XIX. — COMMON FOODS GROUPED ACCORDING TO THE AMOUNT OF CALCIUM (IN GRAMS) IN THE 100-CALORIE PORTIONS (Arranged from tables in Sherman's *Chemistry of Food and Nutrition*) FOODS ARE LISTED IN THE ORDER OF AMOUNT CONTAINED

	VEGETABLES	FRUITS	MEAT, FISH, MILK, EGGS, CHEESE, NUTS	GRAIN PRODUCTS	FATS, SUGARS
Over 0.3 gram	Celery, cauliflower, chard		Milk (skimmed, fresh, or dried)		
0.1–0.3 gram	Spinach, kohlrabi, lettuce, rhubarb, dandelions, turnips, cabbages, carrots, asparagus, string beans	Strawberries	Buttermilk, clams, cheese, milk (con'd — unsweetened), milk (whole), oysters		
0.05–0.1 gram	Parsnips, cucumbers, pumpkin, Brussels sprouts, radishes, onions, beets, tomatoes	Oranges, lemons, raspberries, figs	Milk (sweetened — con'd)	Cottonseed meal, Boston brown bread	Molasses, cream (18%)
0.025–0.05 gram	Beans (white), eggplant, squash, peppers (green), lentils, peas	Currants, cantaloupe, olives, pineapple, grapefruit, cranberries, peaches, watermelon, blackberries, blueberries, cherries	Eggs, fish (lean), hazelnuts, almonds		Maple syrup
0.01–0.025 gram	Beans (Lima), potatoes	Pears, plums, apricots, dates, grapes, raisins, prunes, apples	Fish (oily), cocoa, chocolate, chestnuts, peanuts, walnuts, pecans		
Below 0.01 gram	Corn	Bananas	Veal, beef, fowl, pork, lamb, mutton, coconut	Bread (rye), flour (rye, white, entire wheat), crackers (soda), farina, corn meal, tapioca, rice, hominy	Bacon, butter, honey, sugar, lard

ties might be made attractive for a time, but the continued use of them, month after month, year in and year out, would soon lead to monotony. It is far more interesting and much safer to include a quart of milk daily for each growing child, which will provide his entire calcium need, and at least a pint for each adult, which will supply about four fifths of his requirement; with this amount of calcium supplied through milk it is safe to assume that the remainder will be met by other foods; no further planning for calcium will then be necessary.

Phosphorus. In addition to its use in bones and teeth, phosphorus is necessary for all cell growth and for the proper functioning of all cells. It is therefore essential in all processes in the body and helps to maintain a proper balance between acids and bases. Its presence is also necessary for the production of energy. Phosphorus is a very important element in good nutrition. It does not, however, need the careful attention which must be given to calcium, because it is so widely distributed in the food world that diets are seldom deficient in it.

A safety phosphorus allowance. All evidence collected seems to indicate that 1.32 grams of phosphorus will cover the needs of, and provide a margin of safety for, an average-sized man weighing 154 pounds; in other words, for every pound of body weight, a man should have about 0.009 gram of phosphorus. Like calcium, phosphorus needs do not vary with activity or with sex, but they increase or decrease according to weight. To find the amount of phosphorus for any given person, multiply his weight in pounds by 0.009, and the result will be the safety phosphorus allowance in grams for that person.

The amount of phosphorus specified above is sufficient to maintain grown tissues in good condition, but it does not allow for growth.   As boys and girls need more phosphorus in proportion to weight than do men and women, Sherman suggests that one gram of phosphorus be taken daily per individual throughout the growing period.

Sources of phosphorus. Phosphorus is found in almost all foods, but its chief sources are milk, cheese, eggs, meat, dry beans and peas, nuts, and the whole grain products, such as oatmeal, whole wheat, and barley. This list corresponds very closely with the foods valuable for protein.   Chart XV represents the

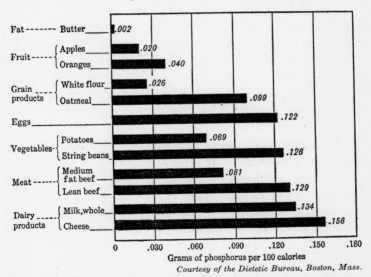

Courtesy of the Dietetic Bureau, Boston, Mass.

Chart XV. — A comparison of some common foods on the basis of the number of grams of phosphorus per 100 Calories

TABLE XX. — COMMON FOODS GROUPED AND LISTED IN THE ORDER OF THE AMOUNT OF PHOSPHORUS (IN GRAMS) IN THE 100-CALORIE PORTIONS (Arranged from tables in Sherman's *Chemistry of Food and Nutrition*)

	VEGETABLES	FRUITS	MEAT, FISH, MILK, EGGS, CHEESE, NUTS	GRAIN PRODUCTS	FATS, SUGARS
Above 0.2 gram	Brussels sprouts, spinach, pumpkin, lettuce, celery, cauliflower		Oysters, clams (long), fish (lean), buttermilk, milk (skimmed, fresh, or dried)	Cottonseed meal	
0.1–0.2 gram	Cucumbers, kohlrabi, asparagus, peppers (green), beans (white), rhubarb, string beans, lentils, eggplant, peas, dandelions, parsnips, turnips, tomatoes, chard, corn, carrots		Cheese, veal, fish (oily), milk (con'd — unsweetened), cocoa, milk (fresh—whole), beef (lean), eggs, clams (round)	Graham flour	
0.05–0.1 gram	Radishes, beans (Lima), onions, cabbage, beets, potatoes (white) squash	Raspberries, strawberries, currants, pineapple, blackberries, peaches	Pork (lean), fowl, beef (med. fat), chocolate, milk (con'd — sweetened), almonds, peanuts, lamb, mutton, hazelnuts, pecans	Oatmeal, shredded wheat, Boston brown bread, graham bread, rye flour, entire wheat bread, entire wheat flour, buckwheat flour, rice (brown), rye head, corn meal	
0.01–0.05 gram	Potatoes (sweet)	Lemons, apricots, pears, oranges, cherries, cantaloupe, plums, raisins, figs, grapefruit, prunes, grapes, bananas, cranberries, apples, dates, blackberries, watermelon	Pork (fat), chestnuts, coconut, walnuts	Macaroni, white bread, farina, hominy, rice (white), white flour, crackers (soda), tapioca	Cream, bacon, molasses
0.001–0.01 gram		Olives			Honey, maple syrup, butter

relative value of various types of foods for phosphorus, and Table XX gives foods grouped according to relative phosphorus values. By comparing Chart XV with Chart XIV it will be seen that phosphorus is found more widely distributed in foods than is calcium; therefore the provision of adequate phosphorus presents a simpler problem in the diet. Tables XXII, XXIII, XXIV, XXV, and XXVI give the grams of phosphorus per 100-Calorie portion of each common food.

IRON AND IODINE

Iron. Iron helps to make good red blood. It is a necessary part of all cell life and of all the activities within the body. The presence of iron in hemoglobin gives the latter the power to unite with oxygen in the lungs and thus to carry it to the tissues; in the tissues, oxygen helps in the production of energy, and takes part in all the processes which make life possible. If the amount of iron in the diet is inadequate, there soon appear easy fatigue, lassitude, and a general feeling of inability to move about or work as usual.

A safety iron allowance. As very little iron is stored in the body, it is important to have each day's food supply the amount needed daily. Sherman has suggested 0.015 gram of iron per day for adults weighing 154 pounds, or 0.0001 gram per pound of body weight. For growing children he suggests an allowance of 0.005 gram per 1000 Calories.

Foods valuable for iron. Eggs, lean meat, whole grains (such as oatmeal and whole wheat), dried fruits (especially prunes), and such vegetables as spinach, lettuce, chard, asparagus, dandelions, turnip tops, cabbage, string beans, Brussels sprouts, white potatoes, and dry beans and peas are the foods richest in iron. While milk, weight for weight, does not contain so much iron as do some of the other foods, the iron present is in a form easily utilized in the tissues, and, since a quart of milk per day provides one fifth of the total daily

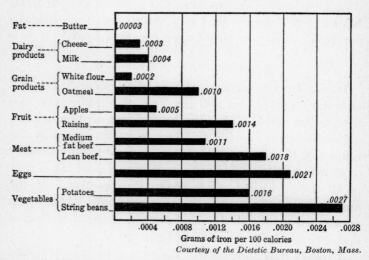

Courtesy of the Dietetic Bureau, Boston, Mass.

Chart XVI. — A comparison of some common foods on the basis of the number of grams of iron per 100 Calories

requirement for a seven- to ten-year-old child, milk may also be considered as one of the valuable sources of iron.

Chart XVI represents the relative value of some common foods for iron; Table XXI gives foods grouped according to relative iron values; while Tables XXII, XXIII, XXIV, XXV, and XXVI give the grams of iron per 100 Calories of some common foods.

TABLE XXI. — Common Foods Grouped and Listed in the Order of the Amount of Iron (in Grams) in the 100-Calorie Portions (Arranged from tables in Sherman's *Chemistry of Food and Nutrition*).

	Vegetables	Fruits	Meat, Fish, Milk, Eggs, Cheese, Nuts	Grain Products	Fats, Sugars
Above 0.005 gram	Spinach, lettuce, chard				
0.002–0.005 gram	Asparagus, dandelions, rhubarb, cabbage, Brussels sprouts (?), string beans, celery, lentils, peppers (green), radishes, cauliflower, shell beans	Strawberries	Eggs		Molasses
0.001–0.002 gram	Kohlrabi, eggplant, tomatoes, peas, potatoes (white), beets, carrots, squash, turnips, cucumbers, onions, pumpkin	Lemons, raisins, cranberries, pineapple, blueberries, blackberries, prunes, figs, olives, watermelon	Beef, pork (lean), fowl, fish (lean), lamb	Boston brown bread, entire wheat flour, shredded wheat, graham flour, graham bread, oatmeal	Maple syrup
0.0005–0.001 gram	Parsnips, corn	Currants, dates, raspberries, cantaloupe, peaches, bananas, grapefruit, plums, apples, apricots, cherries, pears	Mutton, buttermilk, milk (skimmed), pork (fat), fish (oily), almonds, hazelnuts, cocoa	Entire wheat bread, entire wheat flour, rice (brown), tapioca	
0.0001–0.0005 gram	Potatoes (sweet)	Oranges, grapes	Milk (fresh, whole), milk (con'd), chocolate, peanuts, pecans, cheese, chestnuts, coconut, walnuts	Rye flour, white bread, rye bread, crackers (soda), buckwheat flour, corn meal, hominy, macaroni, rice (white), farina, white flour	Honey, bacon, cream, butter

Iodine.   Iodine is present in the body in such minute quantities that for a long time its presence was overlooked.   Then it was discovered that the thyroid gland, in which iodine is located, does not function properly when even this small amount falls below normal.   At certain periods of life, particularly at the time of adolescence, the ill effects of insufficient iodine are felt. Adolescent boys and girls should be sure they are receiving an adequate amount of iodine.

In most parts of the country the drinking water, milk supply, and green vegetables will provide all the iodine needed by the body, but in certain parts of this country and of other countries, where the soil is poor in iodine, the drinking water and the products of the soil do not contain even the small amount necessary for health.   In these districts simple goiter is very common.   In the goiter belts, iodine is often added to the water or to the table salt as a preventive measure, but if one lives in a goiter district where these precautions are neglected, iodine should be taken in some form recommended by a physician.   This is especially important for growing children and for adolescents.   Even in districts where simple goiter is not common, it is well to eat freely of the foods known to contain iodine; these are milk, green vegetables, and sea food.   Sea weed, which is used in making Irish moss gelatin, is a very rich source of iodine.

PROBLEMS

37. How much milk does it take to supply one gram of calcium? How many oranges?   How much cauliflower?

38. How much lean meat does it take to supply one gram of phosphorus?   How much lean fish?   How many potatoes?   How

much spinach does it take to supply 0.015 gram of iron? How many eggs? How many oranges? How many raisins?

39. Plan for a high-school girl a day's meals, consisting of a variety of foods which will furnish proper amounts of calcium, phosphorus, and iron. Weigh out the foods (raw materials).

40. Prepare several of these menus in class; retain all the mineral elements possible by careful methods of cooking.

41. How do the amounts of calcium, phosphorus, and iron-rich foods in these meals compare with the amounts of these foods in your own diet for any one day?

42. Calculate the amounts of phosphorus, calcium, and iron needed daily by each member of your family. What is the total amount of each mineral element required by your family? Record in your notebook.

43. To become familiar with the foods that are rich in phosphorus, calcium, and iron:

Make a list of the foods valuable for each of these mineral elements. Record them in your notebook. Select from the list some common, inexpensive foods that you are not in the habit of eating. Plan to cook and serve these foods at home. Report your experiment.

QUESTIONS

1. What is meant by mineral elements?

2. Name the mineral elements which are known to exist in the body and which must be replaced by food?

3. How does an insufficient amount of these elements affect the body?

4. What foods have an acid influence in the body?
What foods have an alkaline influence in the body?

5. Calcium, phosphorus and iron are the minerals especially needed by the body. What special functions has each in the body?

6. How is the body supplied with iodine?

7. Completion test.

    A boy or girl needs —— grams of calcium daily.

    A boy or girl needs —— grams of phosphorus daily.

    A boy or girl needs —— grams of iron daily.

    To find the amount of calcium needed by an adult daily, multiply his weight by —— grams.

    To find the amount of iron needed by an adult daily, multiply his weight by —— grams.

REFERENCES

For students:

ROSE, MARY S. *Feeding the Family*, third edition, Chapter I, pages 18 to 24; Chapter III, pages 85 to 88. The Macmillan Company (1929).

SANSUM, D. W. *The Normal Diet*, revised edition, Chapters III, IV, and VII. C. V. Mosby Company (1927).

For teachers:

ROSE, MARY S. *Foundations of Nutrition*, Chapters VII and VIII. The Macmillan Company (1927).

SANSUM, D. W. *The Normal Diet*, revised edition, Chapters III, IV, and VII. C. V. Mosby Company (1927).

SHERMAN, H. C. *Chemistry of Food and Nutrition*, third edition, Chapters IX, X, XI, and XII. The Macmillan Company (1926).

CHAPTER VI

VITAMINS

A VITAMIN is like an electric spark that helps the whole mechanism to operate properly. The vitamin family has six members called A, B, C, D, E, and G. Each is essential for growth, yet each has special duties to perform. Vitamins A and C defend the body against infections; vitamin A guards the eyes, ears, and the respiratory tract, while vitamin C protects bones and teeth. Vitamins B and G help to control the nerves and digestion. Vitamin D is necessary for the formation of strong bones and decay-resisting teeth, and it probably helps to keep adults in good condition. Vitamin E is concerned with reproduction. An insufficient amount of any one of the vitamins will result in some physical abnormality.

It was formerly supposed that energy foods, proteins, and mineral elements were the only food substances necessary to keep us alive and well, but, after repeated failures to find a combination of these foodstuffs which would be perfect for growth and health, investigators grew suspicious, because the purer the substances they fed their experimental animals, the more likely the animals were to die. Finally, in 1912, there was discovered the existence of another factor which was helping all these food substances to work properly and without which they could not permanently support good nutrition. Because of its relation to life it was called a vitamin (from the Latin word *vita*, which means life).

Since 1912 scientists have found several other vitamins, each of which is essential for growth, yet each has its own special part to play in maintaining life and making health possible. Because vitamins prevent certain diseases and help to regulate the various internal processes, McCollum has very aptly referred to them as protective substances, but, to distinguish one vitamin from another, each is designated by a letter of the alphabet. At present, the known vitamins are called A, B, C, D, E, and G. (The letter F has been used in different ways and at present is not in general use for a vitamin.)

Vitamin A

Importance of vitamin A. Vitmin A, like each of the other factors, is necessary for the normal growth of children. It is essential for good nutrition and for a high degree of resistance to infections in both children and adults. With an abundance of A, animals grow faster during the growing period; they reach maturity earlier, and maintain physical vigor for a longer period with less danger of diseases than those on diets low in vitamin A.

Effect of insufficient vitamin A. With complete absence of A there can be neither growth nor life, but, as with mineral elements, there is little danger of a diet without some A; our chief anxiety is about a continued daily intake below that needed for optimum development and for protection from disease. The food of two boys or two girls may be so similar as to seem to the casual observer identical in make-up, yet it may so differ in the amount of A present as to cause one boy or girl to grow more rapidly than the other; or each may receive enough A to make growth average for age, but one may have too little to build tissues that can withstand disease. Charts XVII and XVIII represent the rate of growth of rats fed with varying amounts of vitamin A; the rats receiving a liberal amount of this factor grew normally, while the ones with a small amount of it

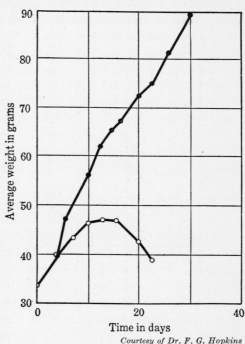

Chart XVII. — Growth curve of rats; lower curve shows the effect of an artificial diet with no vitamin A; the upper curve shows the effect of the addition of 2 c.c. of milk to the artificial diet

failed to grow, their eyes became swollen, and their hair rough and lusterless.

When the diet contains a surplus of vitamin A (an intake over and above that needed for growth and resistance), the excess will be stored in the tissues and called upon when a person needs more of this protective quality than his food supplies. But as this storehouse is depleted, vitality and resistance gradually decrease also; at the same time there appear many of the common symptoms recognized as part of a general run-down condition, such as rough, lusterless, and falling hair, a poor appetite, digestive trouble, and infections of the eyes, ears, nose, throat, sinuses, the whole respiratory tract, the skin, and the bladder. Because boys and girls usually have sufficient A in their daily food to support considerable gain in weight and to make them vigorous enough to enter into games and sports, a deficiency of A is

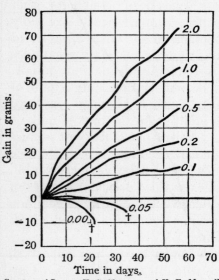

Courtesy of Doctors H. C. Sherman and H. E. Munsell

Chart XVIII. — Variations in the rate of growth due to differences in the amount of vitamin A; the figures at the right hand end of the growth lines indicate the amount of tomato fed as a source of vitamin A

easily overlooked until its ill effects appear. It is best to have an abundance of vitamin A each and every day.

One of the characteristics of a diet **very low** in vitamin A is an infection of the eyes called xerophthalmia, or conjunctivitis, the end result of which is blindness. As vitamin A cures the condition when not too far advanced, this vitamin is frequently called the antiophthalmic vitamin.

A safety allowance of vitamin A. Although we are unable to state the amount of any vitamin required with as much definiteness as has been possible for other foodstuffs, we recognize their importance in the daily diet. For safety, we recommend one quart of milk and a generous serving of one or more green leafy vegetables each day as a means of introducing adequate vitamin A. If a person is able, or advised, to take only a pint of milk daily, then for safety, he should have at least two sources of vitamin A in addition to the pint of milk.

Sources of vitamin A. Milk is one of the best sources of vitamin A because it can be taken in considerable quantity without inconvenience; egg yolk, cod-liver oil, and green leafy vegetables are also excellent sources of this food factor. The relative value of most common foods for vitamin A will be found in Tables XXII, XXIII, XXIV, XXV, and XXVI.

So far as we know, all green leaves and almost all yellow-colored foods are valuable for vitamin A. Carrots, butter, cod-liver oil, and egg yolk, all yellow-colored, are among the richest known sources of vitamin A, the amount of A varying with the intensity of the color. Yellow corn is richer in A than white corn, yellow turnip than white turnip, and sweet potato than white potato. Tomatoes with their bright red color are by far the best source of A among fruits. Beets, on the other hand, are a poor source of A.

Dark green leaves contain many times more A than very pale or white leaves, even on the same plant. For instance, the outside green leaves of cabbage or lettuce contain more A than the bleached and pale green leaves toward the center of the head. Spinach, green string beans, and young peas are much richer in A than is white cabbage; also, the thinner the leaf, the more A contained per unit of weight.

Effect of heat on vitamin A. The effectiveness of A is lessened by heat in the presence of air, the amount of destruction being in direct relation to the amount of air present and the length of heating. For this reason food cooked in a vacuum or canned in a closed jar has more of its vitamin value retained than the same food cooked in an open kettle or pan.

Vitamins B and G

Vitamins B and G are so similar in many of their functions that as yet the difference between them is not very clearly defined. They are both essential for growth, they both help in the control of the nerves, and they both play a large part in digestion.

Vitamin B. The importance of vitamin B was discovered in an interesting way. Pigeons fed on white rice (rice with the outside coating removed) developed a disease called beri-beri, or polyneuritis. In this disease paralysis occurs, with loss of nerve control, but when the pigeons were given water in which the rice bran (the part removed in making white rice) had been soaking, they were able to walk in a few hours. This incident led scientists to investigate the difference in composition between the outside and the inside of rice and other grains. They found none of this protective quality in the inner part of rice or other grains, but the brown layer (or outer coating) of all grains contained the same curative property as the bran of the rice; because this substance cured polyneuritis, they called it the antineuritic vitamin, but more recently it has been called vitamin B.

In addition to its power to influence the nerves, vitamin B is essential for growth, for good digestion, and for reproduction. With too little B there occurs retarded growth, the amount of retardation depending on the amount of B present; there will be disturbances of the digestive tract which begin with a poor appetite, develop into indigestion, and end in serious gastro-intestinal trouble. As it is not stored in the tissues, the ill effects of diets low in B are felt more quickly than are the results from diets low in A.

Vitamin G. In addition to its functions in growth, vitamin G is known to be necessary for the prevention of pellagra, a disease more common in certain parts of the country than in others; some of the characteristics of a deficiency of G are disturbances of the nervous and digestive systems and sometimes of the skin. As B also influences these systems, and as G has been discovered so recently, the distinction between the functions of the two vitamins is not entirely clear as yet.

Sources of vitamins B and G. Because vitamins B and G are so closely associated in foods, it has not as yet been determined which foods are best for B and which are more valuable for G, except in a few important cases. Vitamins B and G are known to exist in whole wheat and probably in all whole grain products, in green leafy vegetables, and in cow's milk. In general, milk, whole or skimmed, and green leafy vegetables

are richer in G than in B, while whole grain products
are richer in B than in G.   Accordingly, whole wheat
bread and milk supplement each other with regard to
these two vitamins and make an excellent combination
for growth.   Foods that have been highly refined in the
manufacturing process, such as polished rice, patent
flours, new-process cornmeal, sugar, olive oil, and other
commercial fats, are likely to be deficient in both
vitamin B and vitamin G.   Tables XXII, XXIII,
XXIV, XXV, and XXVI give the relative value of
common foods for vitamins B and G.

Amounts of B and G for safety.   These two vitamins
seem to be very widely distributed in the food world,
and, for this reason, diets are not so apt to be deficient in
them as in vitamins A and C.   There is little danger of
having a diet with no B or G; as with other factors,
the danger lies in an amount which, although high
enough to promote growth, is too low for good health.
Since we have no way of measuring the amounts of the
various vitamins required for health, but since they
are known to play such an important part in both
health and growth, we can only recommend a generous
amount of the foods rich in them.

Effect of water on vitamins B and G.   These vitamins are soluble in water, and much may be lost during
the cooking process unless special precautions are taken
to preserve them.   To prevent loss of this valuable
factor, vegetables should be cooked whole, with the skins
on, in as little water as possible, and only long enough
to make them tender.   The water in which pared
vegetables are cooked should be saved to use in soups,
stews, and gravies.

Vitamin C

Importance of vitamin C. Vitamin C, like the other members of the vitamin family, is necessary for good health and vigor. Its special functions seem to be the

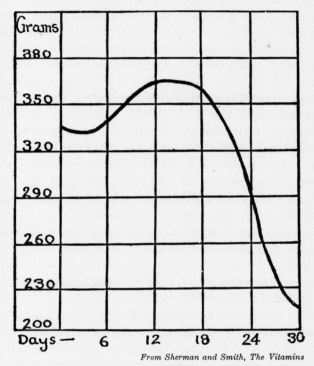

From Sherman and Smith, The Vitamins

Chart XIX. — The result of too little vitamin C

formation of bones and teeth and the development of resistance to disease for both children and adults. Chart XIX represents the fate of guinea pigs kept on a diet free of vitamin C. With no C there is no life; with an amount of C which will support life but which is too low for vigorous health, the teeth decay easily, there will be irritability, restlessness, easy fatigue, lack of pep and vigor, headaches, sallow and muddy complexions, loss of weight, loss of appetite, slow healing of cuts and bruises, loosening of the teeth, fragile bones that break easily, and stiffness, swelling, and soreness of joints. Much of the so-called rheumatism common in late winter and early spring is probably a mild form of scurvy due to a lack of vitamin C. Because C will cure scurvy, this vitamin is sometimes called the antiscorbutic vitamin.

Sources of vitamin C. Tomatoes, raw spinach, raw cabbage, raw carrots, raw green peppers, and citrus fruits, such as oranges, lemons, grapefruit, and tangerines, are among the richest sources of C. The amount of C varies with the age of the vegetable; young green leaves are richer in it than the older leaves; young carrots contain more C than older carrots; young peas are more valuable for C than older peas.

Weight for weight, potatoes are not so rich in C as the foods just mentioned, but, when used in large quantities, they may provide a very considerable part of the total C requirement for the day. A cooked potato, a raw apple, and a raw banana are about equally valuable for vitamin C. Ordinary dry legumes contain no C, but bean sprouts are rich in it. Raw milk, obtained from cows feeding on green grass or on green fodder, is a good source of C, but milk in general must be regarded as a variable source, not to be depended on as a main supply of vitamin C. White sugar, fats, oils, eggs, meat, fish, and grain products, such as bread, cereals, rice, and macaroni, are not good sources of vitamin C.

A safety allowance of vitamin C. For optimum protection and safety it is advisable to have at least two excellent sources of vitamin C in the diet daily. Nursing mothers especially need an abundance of C to enable them to provide the quality of milk which will build strong bones and sound teeth for the baby. Tables XXII, XXIII, XXIV, XXV, and XXVI give the relative value of the common foods for vitamin C.

Effect of heat, water, and alkali on vitamin C. Vitamin C is gradually destroyed by heat in the presence of air. This makes it desirable to have in the diet each day at least one uncooked food rich in vitamin C. However, those vegetables which become tender in a short time (such as young carrots, peas, potatoes, and tomatoes), and those which can be cooked without water (such as spinach) still retain important amounts of C, even when cooked according to the usual home methods. Vitamin C in tomatoes is less easily affected by heat than is vitamin C in most other foods.

Raw cabbage contains twenty times as much of this protective quality as does the same amount of cabbage cooked one hour; raw cabbage contains twice as much C as do raw potatoes, but cooked potatoes contain from two to six times as much vitamin C as cooked cabbage, because of the greater surface exposure in the cabbage and therefore the greater loss through solubility and the destruction by heat.

As C is soluble in water, much of it may be lost during the cooking of vegetables. All vegetables should be cooked whole with the skins on where possible. Vitamin C is more rapidly destroyed in the presence of alkali; therefore baking soda should not be used in cooking vegetables.

Vitamin D

Vitamin D helps to make strong bones and teeth and to increase the resistance of the respiratory tract to colds, pneumonia, and other diseases, but to produce these results vitamin D must be given during the early years of life, while the bones and tissues are being formed.

Effect of a deficiency of D. When babies have too little vitamin D, rickets will develop, even though calcium and phosphorus are abundantly supplied. With an insufficient amount of D during the first year of life, the structure of the teeth will be such that they decay easily, and the bones of the chest will form a flattened chest cavity, which will interfere with breathing and chest expansion later, thereby lessening physical vigor. Illustration No. 6 shows this deformity in a rat fed on a diet low in vitamin D, during its period of growth. At the left of the picture is the chest cavity of a rat fed a normal diet containing plenty of vitamin D; the ribs are regular and the chest cavity well formed. At the right is a picture of a rickety rat; the chest cavity is very evidently deformed, the shoulders are rounded, and the ribs have knobs or beadings on them, a characteristic of rickets. Bowed legs are not the only manifestation of rickets; in fact, crooked legs are much less serious than a deformed chest with weakened tissues.

Sources of vitamin D. The best source of vitamin D is cod-liver oil; egg yolk, whole milk, cream, fresh green leaves (if grown in the sun) are also important

sources of it.   Another **very** valuable way of introducing vitamin D into the system is through exposure of
the skin to the direct rays of the sun, whereupon there
will be formed from a substance in the skin, vitamin D,

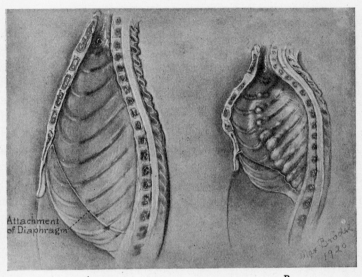

A   B

Courtesy of E. V. McCollum, Ph.D.

Illustration No. 6. — Influence of vitamin D.   At the left of the picture
   (*A*) is an illustration of a normal chest of a rat that had had plenty
   of vitamin D; at the right (*B*) is a picture of the chest cavity of a rat
   on a diet lacking in D during the growing period

which will enter the circulation, reach the tissues, and
perform the same work as vitamin D taken in through
the food.

Because vitamin D is so essential, because mother's
milk may not contain enough of it, because mothers
are often careless about giving the baby his sun bath,

because cod-liver oil is such an excellent source of vitamins A and D, many physicians recommend cod-liver oil for all babies and small children through the first five or six years of life.

VITAMIN E

Vitamin E has been more recently discovered and therefore less thoroughly studied than vitamins A, B, C, and D, but E is known to exist and to be associated with reproduction. Vitamin E is widely distributed in foods, and there is little danger of a deficiency of it.

PROBLEMS

44. List the foods valuable for vitamin A, vitamins B and G, vitamin C, and vitamin D. Record these lists in your notebook.

45. Arrange an exhibit of foods which will illustrate the sources of each vitamin.

46. Select the foods which will insure an adequate vitamin supply for a high-school girl or boy for a day.

TABLE XXII. — AMOUNT (IN GRAMS) OF PROTEIN, CALCIUM, PHOS-
PHOROUS, AND IRON IN 100-CALORIE PORTIONS; AND VITAMIN
VALUES OF THE COMMON FOODS (Copied from *Sherman's Chemistry
of Food and Nutrition* and Rose's *Laboratory Handbook for Dietetics*)

VEGETABLES

	PRO-TEIN	CAL-CIUM	PHOS-PHO-RUS	IRON	VITAMIN A	VITAMINS B–G	VITAMIN C
	Grams	*Grams*	*Grams*	*Grams*			
Asparagus . .	8.1	.122	.177	.0045	+ to ++	+++	*
Beans							
kidney, dried	5.8	.040	.143	.0022	+	+++	+
Lima . . .	5.8	.020	.096	.0020	+	+++	*
string . .	5.6	.110	.126	.0027	++	++	+++
white . .	6.5	.047	.137	.0020	+	+++	*

TABLE XXII (*Continued*)

	PRO-TEIN	CAL-CIUM	PHOS-PHO-RUS	IRON	VIT-AMIN A	VIT-AMINS B–G	VIT-AMIN C
	Grams	*Grams*	*Grams*	*Grams*			
Beets	3.5	.064	.084	.0013	+		+
Brussels sprouts	7.3	.086	.380	.0035	++	+++	+
Cabbage	5.1	.143	.092	.0035	+	++	+++
Carrots	2.4	.124	.101	.0013	+++	++	++
Cauliflower	5.9	.403	.200	.0020	+	++	+
Celery	1.3	.421	.201	.0027	–	++	++
Chard	8.4	.393	.105	.0066	++	+	*
Corn	3.1	.006	.102	.0008	+	++	*
Cucumbers	4.6	.090	.191	.0012	+	+	++
Dandelions	3.9	.172	.117	.0044	++	++	+
Eggplant	4.3	.041	.122	.0018	+	+	*
Endive	7.1	.743	.893	.0057	+	++	+
Kale	6.7	.416	.118	.0061	++	++	+
Kohl-rabi	6.5	.249	.186	.0019	*	*	+
Lentils	7.4	.031	.126	.0025	+	++	–
Lettuce	6.3	.224	.224	.0037	+ to ++	++	+++
Mushrooms	7.8	.038	.241	———	–	++	*
Okra	4.2	.213	.057	———	*	+++?	*
Onions	3.3	.069	.093	.0010	– to +	+	++
Parsnips	2.5	.091	.117	.0009	– to +	++	*
Peas	6.9	.026	.127	.0017	++	++	+++
Peas, split	6.9	.024	.112	.0016	+	++	–
Peppers, green	4.6	.034	.145	.0022	++	++	+++
Potatoes, sweet	1.5	.016	.037	.0004	++	++	++
white	2.7	.016	.069	.0016	+	++	++
Pumpkin	3.9	.090	.229	.0013	+	+	+
Radishes	4.4	.073	.098	.0021	– to +	+	*
Rhubarb	2.6	.189	.134	.0043	*	*	+
Spinach	8.8	.281	.285	.0150	+++	+++	+++
Squash summer	3.1	.039	.035	.0013	*	*	*
winter	3.1	.039	.061	.0013	++	*	–
Tomatoes	4.0	.050	.113	.0018	++	++	+++
Turnips	3.3	.161	.117	.0013	– to +	++	++
Watercress	3.2	.850	.023	.0086	*	*	*

Table XXIII. — Amount (in Grams) of Protein, Calcium, Phosphorus, and Iron in 100-Calorie Portions; and Vitamin Values of the Common Foods (Copied from Sherman's *Chemistry of Food and Nutrition* and Rose's *Laboratory Handbook for Dietetics*)

FRUITS

	Protein	Calcium	Phosphorus	Iron	Vitamin A	Vitamins B–G	Vitamin C
	Grams	*Grams*	*Grams*	*Grams*			
Apples . . .	0.6	.012	.020	.0005	+	+ to ++	++
Apricots . .	1.9	.023	.044	.0005	*	*	*
Apricots, dried	1.7	.024	.042	.0005	*	*	*
Avocado (Alligator pear) . .	1.1	.076	.050	.0065	+	++	*
Bananas . .	1.3	.009	.031	.0006	++	+ to ++	++
Blackberries .	2.3	.029	.058	.0010	*	+	+
Blueberries .	0.8	.027	.011	.0012	*	*	*
Cantaloupe .	1.5	.044	.038	.0007	++	++	*
Cherries . .	1.2	.025	.039	.0005	*	*	*
Cranberries .	0.9	.039	.027	.0013	+	*	+
Currants, dry .	0.8	.026	.061	.0009	*	*	*
fresh . .	2.6	.045	.066	.0009	*	*	*
Dates . . .	0.6	.019	.016	.0009	++	*	*
Figs . . .	1.4	.051	.037	.0010	+	*	*
Grapefruit . .	1.2	.040	.036	.0006	+	++	+++
Grapes . . .	1.4	.019	.032	.0003	+	+ to ++	+
Lemons . .	2.3	.081	.049	.0014	+	++	+++
Olives . . .	0.4	.041	.004	.0010	− to +	−	−
Oranges . .	1.6	.088	.040	.0004	+	++	+++
Orange juice .	1.4	.067	.037	.0005	+	++	+++
Peaches . .	1.7	.038	.057	.0007	+	+ to ++	++
Pears . . .	1.0	.024	.041	.0005	*	+	+
Pineapple . .	0.9	.041	.064	.0012	++	++	++
Plums . . .	1.2	.024	.038	.0006	*	*	*
Prunes . . .	0.7	.018	.035	.0010	+++	++	−
Raisins . . .	0.8	.019	.038	.0006	−	+	−
Raspberries .	2.6	.074	.078	.0009	*	*	++
Strawberries .	2.6	.104	.072	.0021	*	+	+ to ++
Watermelon .	1.3	.038	.010	.0010	*	*	*

TABLE XXIV. — AMOUNT (IN GRAMS) OF PROTEIN, CALCIUM, PHOS-
PHORUS, AND IRON IN 100-CALORIE PORTIONS; AND VITAMIN
VALUES OF THE COMMON FOODS (Copied from Sherman's *Chem-
istry of Food and Nutrition* and Rose's *Laboratory Handbook for
Dietetics*)

CEREAL PRODUCTS

	PRO-TEIN	CAL-CIUM	PHOS-PHO-RUS	IRON	VITAMIN A	VITAMINS B–G	VITAMIN C
	Grams	*Grams*	*Grams*	*Grams*			
Barley . . .	2.5	.006	.051	.0006	+	++	−
Bread							
Boston brown	2.6	.056	.082	.0013	+	++	−
entire wheat	4.0	.020	.071	.0007	+	++	−
graham . .	3.4	.020	.084	.0010	+	++	−
rye . . .	3.5	.009	.058	.0004	+	++	−
white . .	3.5	.011	.035	.0004	+	+	−
Cornmeal . .	2.6	.005	.053	.0003	− to +	− to +	−
Cottonseed							
meal . .	12.8	.066	.298	. . . . .	+	++	−
Crackers							
soda . . .	2.4	.006	.025	.0004	−	*	−
Farina . . .	3.1	.006	.035	.0002	−	+	−
Flour							
buckwheat .	1.8	.011	.065	.0002	−	− to +	−
entire wheat	3.9	.009	.066	.0007	+	++	−
graham . .	3.7	.011	.101	.0010	+	++	−
rye . . .	2.0	.005	.082	.0004	+	+	−
white . .	3.2	.006	.026	.0002	−	− to +	−
Hominy . .	2.4	.002	.027	.0003	−	−	−
Macaroni . .	3.7	.006	.040	.0003	−	− to +	−
Oatmeal .	4.2	.017	.099	.0010	− to +	++	−
Rice, brown .	2.5	.003	.060	.0006	+	++	−
white . .	2.3	.001	.027	.0003	−	−	−
Shredded							
wheat . .	3.5	.011	.089	.0012	+	++	−
Tapioca . .	0.1	.004	.025	.0005	−	−	−

TABLE XXV. — AMOUNT (IN GRAMS) OF PROTEIN, CALCIUM, PHOS-
PHORUS, AND IRON IN 100-CALORIE PORTIONS; AND VITAMIN
VALUES OF THE COMMON FOODS   (Copied from Sherman's *Chem-
istry of Food and Nutrition* and Rose's *Laboratory Handbook for
Dietetics*)

FATS AND SUGARS

	PRO-TEIN	CAL-CIUM	PHOS-PHO-RUS	IRON	VITAMIN A	VITAMINS B–G	VITAMIN C
	Grams	*Grams*	*Grams*	*Grams*			
Bacon	1.7	.001	.018	.0003	+ to −	+ to ++	?
Butter	0.1	.002	.002	.00003	+++	−	−
Chocolate unsweetened	2.1	.015	.075	.0005	*	*	*
Cocoa	4.4	.023	.143	.0005	*	*	*
Crisco	...	...	...	...	*	*	*
Cream, 18%	1.3	.050	.044	.0001	+++	++	+variable
cream, 40%	0.6	.020	.020	.00005	+++	++	+variable
Honey	0.1	.002	.006	.0003	−	+ ?	−
Maple syrup	...	.037	.003	.0010	−	+	−
Molasses	0.8	.074	.015	.0026	−	+	−
Jam	0.5	.007	.009	.0001	*	*	*
Sugar	...	...	...	...	−	−	−

Table XXVI. — Amount (in Grams) of Protein, Calcium, Phosphorus, and Iron in 100-Calorie Portions; and Vitamin Values of the Common Foods (Copied from Sherman's *Chemistry of Food and Nutrition* and Rose's *Laboratory Handbook for Dietetics*)

Meat, Fish, Eggs, Milk, Cheese, Nuts

	Protein	Calcium	Phosphorus	Iron	Vitamin A	Vitamins B–G	Vitamin C
	Grams	*Grams*	*Grams*	*Grams*			
Almonds . .	3.2	.037	.072	.0006	+	++	− to +
Beef, lean . .	12.0	.007	.129	.0018	− to +	++	− to +
medium fat .	7.5	.004	.081	.0011	+	++	− to +
Beef liver . .	15.8	.014	.171	.0063	++ to +++	++	+
Bologna sausage . .	8.0	.010	.086	.0012	*	*	*
Buttermilk	8.4	.294	.271	.0007	+	++	+variable
Cheese (Am.) .	6.1	.212	.156	.0003	++ to +++	+	*
Chestnuts . .	2.6	.014	.044	.0003	−	+	−
Chicken canned . .	12.3	.004	.129	.0018	*	*	*
Chocolate . .	2.1	.015	.075	.0004	−	*	−
Clams, long .	19.8	.285	.282	.0097	*	*	*
round . .	14.0	.229	.100	.0097	*	*	*
Cocoa . .	4.4	.023	.143	.0005	−	−	−
Coconut . .	1.0	.006	.018	.0003	+	++	*
Eggs, whole .	9.1	.045	.122	.0021	+++	+ to ++	−
yolk . . .	4.3	.036	.118	.0023	+++	++	−
white . .	24.1	.020	.022	.0002	−	*	−
Filberts . .	2.2	.041	.050	.0006	*	*	*
Fish, lean .	22.6	.025	.259	.0012	− to +	+	*
oily . . .	13.3	.015	.153	.0007	+	+	*
Fowl . . .	8.6	.005	.093	.0013	+	*	*
Gelatin . .	25.0	.015	.270	.0038	*	*	*
Ham, lean smoked . .	7.4	.004	.080	.0025	− to +	++	*
Hazelnuts . .	2.2	.041	.050	.0006	*	*	*
Kidney . .	13.5	.008	.145	.0033	++	++	+?
Lamb chops .	6.1	.004	.066	.0009	− to +	+	−
Lamb, leg . .	8.5	.005	.092	.0007	− to +	+	−

TABLE XXVI (*Continued*)

	PRO-TEIN	CAL-CIUM	PHOS-PHO-RUS	IRON	VIT-AMIN A	VIT-AMINS B–G	VIT-AMIN C
	Grams	*Grams*	*Grams*	*Grams*			
Lobster, canned	21.5	.023	.247	.0012	*	*	*
Milk, whole .	4.8	.174	.134	.0004	+++	++	+variable
skimmed .	9.3	.331	.262	.0007	+	++	+variable
condensed							
sweetened	2.7	.096	.072	.0002	+++	++	+variable
unsweet'd	5.8	.189	.146	.0004	+++	++	−?
Mutton . .	6.2	.004	.067	.0009	− to +	++	*
Mutton, leg .	10.4	.006	.112	.0035	− to +	++	*
Oysters . .	12.3	.106	.306	.0089	+	*	+
Peanuts . .	4.7	.013	.073	.0004	+	++	−
Pecans . . .	1.3	.012	.045	.0004	+	+	−
Pork, lean .	9.1	.005	.098	.0014	− to +	+++?	−
medium fat .	4.5	.003	.049	.0007	− to +	+++?	
Sardines							
canned . .	8.5	.013	.136	.0007	*	*	*
Scallops . .	20.1	.022	.231	.0011	*	*	*
Shrimps							
canned . .	22.7	.025	.261	.0013	*	*	*
Tuna fish							
canned, oil .	9.1	.010	.105	.0005	*	*	*
no oil . .	17.6	.019	.201	.0010	*	*	*
Veal . . .	14.5	.008	.156	.0022	− to +	+?	+
Veal, liver . .	15.4	.009	.166	.0023	++to+++	++	+
Walnuts . .	2.6	.013	.015	.0003	+	++	*

Explanation of vitamin values:

− indicates that the vitamin is absent, or present in insignificant amounts only.

+ indicates that food furnishes a significant amount of the vitamin.

++ indicates that the food is a good source of the vitamin.

+++ indicates that the food is an excellent source of the vitamin.

* indicates that present information is not such as to warrant any statement.

QUESTIONS

1. How did scientists happen to discover the substances which they have named vitamins? How long ago was this? How many known vitamins are there known now?

2. What are the special functions of vitamin A?

3. In spite of the fact that vitamin A is widely distributed in foods, there is danger of an insufficient amount in the diet. How is a lack of vitamin A detected? What are the advantages of a good surplus?

4. Tell how vitamin B was discovered. How does an insufficient amount of vitamin B affect the body?

5. What other vitamin is closely related to vitamin B? What foods are rich in vitamin G?

6. What foods are rich in vitamin B? What foods are deficient in vitamin B?

7. Explain the special functions of vitamin C. What foods best supply vitamin C?

8. During what period of life is a deficiency of vitamin D most serious? What are the results when a baby's diet is deficient in vitamin D?

9. Why is a sun bath so beneficial to children? Can anything be substituted for it?

10. What effect has heat and cooking in water upon the different vitamins?

11. Completion test:
One of the best sources of vitamin A is ——.
One of the best sources of vitamin D is —— —— ——.
Vitamins B and G are —— in water.
Vitamin C is —— in water and destroyed by—— and —— ——.

REFERENCES

For students:

McCollum, E. V. and Simmons, N. *Food, Nutrition, and Health.* Lord Baltimore Press (1925).

Rose, Mary S. *Feeding the Family,* third edition, Chapter I, pages 24 to 34; Chapter III, pages 88 and 89; Chapter IV, pages 111 and 112; Chapter V, pages 139 and 140; Appendix, pages 432 to 435. The Macmillan Company (1929).

For teachers:

> EDDY, W. H.   *The Vitamin Manual*, Chapters I and VII.   Williams and Wilkins Co. (1921).
>
> McCOLLUM, E. V. and SIMMONS, N.   *Newer Knowledge of Nutrition*, third edition, Chapters XV, XVI, XIX, XX, and XXI.   The Macmillan Company (1925).
>
> ROSE, MARY S.   *Foundations of Nutrition*, Chapters IX and X. The Macmillan Company (1927).
>
> SHERMAN, H. C.   *Chemistry of Food and Nutrition*, third edition, Chapters XIV, XV, XVI, XVII, and XVIII.   The Macmillan Company (1926).

CHAPTER VII

FOOD SELECTION

As an aid in the planning of meals, three methods are suggested as follows:

Food selection according to groups

Food selection according to the number of Calories, grams of protein, calcium, phosphorus, and iron, with consideration also of vitamins

Food selection according to the number of shares of each of the food factors mentioned above, with consideration also of vitamins

Food Needs Summarized

To plan a diet that will enable you to feel best, accomplish most, and reach the desired goal with least friction, it is necessary to have some basis for the selection of food. The previous discussions of food values and body needs supply the foundation for intelligent meal planning, but they may have seemed confusing and difficult to put into actual practice. Therefore this chapter is intended to summarize the various points and to show how to simplify the work involved.

The one common problem which must be considered in every individual or family diet scheme, is the daily provision of foodstuffs, as follows:

For every adult:

Energy	According to weight and activity
Protein	0.5 gram per pound of body weight
Calcium	0.005 gram per pound of body weight
Phosphorus	0.01 gram per pound of body weight
Iron	0.0001 gram per pound of body weight

For every boy and girl through the growing period:

Energy	According to age, weight, and activity
Protein	30 grams per 1000 Calories, or as in Table XVIII
Calcium	1 gram per individual
Phosphorus	1 gram per individual
Iron	0.005 gram (or more) per 1000 Calories

In addition to the above requirements, each person, of whatever age, needs vitamins which may be supplied through:

Two foods daily which are rich in vitamin A
Two foods daily which are rich in vitamins B and G
One food daily which is rich in vitamin C (uncooked)
Plenty of sunshine to produce vitamin D

SELECTION OF FOODS

Three methods are offered whereby it is possible to plan satisfactory meals. These methods are as follows:

I. Selection of foods according to food groups

II. Selection of foods according to food groups, with calculation of food values in terms of Calories and grams of protein, calcium, phosphorus, and iron, with consideration also of foods valuable for vitamins

III. Selection of foods according to food groups, with calculation of food values in terms of shares, in which case also the vitamin values must be considered

METHOD I

Selection of foods according to food groups. This is the simplest and perhaps the only way in which to explain good food selection to the layman who has no knowledge of food values and who has no time in which to make adequate calculations. The plan is as indicated below.

Include Each Day Some Food from Each Food Group

Group 1. Milk	Allow from one pint to one quart per person per day. A quart is especially desirable for all children through the growing period and for those needing special nourishment.
Group 2. Meat, fish, eggs, cheese, dry beans, dry peas	One food from this group, the amount varying with the age and the other foods in the diet.
Group 3. Vegetables and fruits	Generous servings of two or more vegetables a day; one of these should be a green leafy vegetable at least every other day. Some fresh fruit daily, with citrus fruit or tomato at least three or four times a week.
Group 4. Grain products	Generous amounts at each meal for growing children and for underweights. Those inclined to be stout should use these foods cautiously.
Group 5. Fats and sugars.	Use cautiously.

The simplicity of the above method recommends it for general use, especially in the planning of meals for families or for large groups. Its chief disadvantage lies in the fact that it is unsafe for a person who is unfamiliar with food values to deviate from the rule, though such deviations are possible, lest he plan meals which are not adequate in all food factors.

For instance, it is quite possible for a person to obtain

all his protein from milk plus such amounts as may be provided by potatoes and grain products, thus making meat and eggs unnecessary; the kind of vegetables which should be selected will vary with the other foods in the meal; also one may obtain vitamin C from green leaves instead of from fruit. These and many other variations are possible, but to name them all would make the scheme too cumbersome. Individual needs are best provided through a calculation of food values, as described in the next two methods, or through such a thorough acquaintance with food values that one can tell at a glance whether or not any one diet will provide sufficient amounts of the various food factors.

METHOD II

Calculation of food values in terms of grams. This method involves much calculation, but if carefully and faithfully applied to a number of diets, it will give a familiarity with food values which is invaluable and which will soon make it safe to apply variations to Method I. In planning meals according to the number of Calories and grams of protein, phosphorus, calcium, and iron, the procedure is somewhat as follows:

1. Use the food groups as a basis for arranging a combination of foods which seems satisfactory.
2. Calculate the food value in terms of Calories, protein, calcium, phosphorus, and iron.
3. Determine the amount of each food factor required by the person or persons for whom the food is intended, and compare these amounts with the food value of the diet as planned.

4. Through trial and error, add, subtract, and substitute foods until the desired balance is acquired.

As the above method is the one used throughout the first half of this text, it needs no further comment.

METHOD III

Calculating diets by means of shares. Valuable as is the previous method for planning an appropriate diet, it involves much calculation, and Mrs. Rose, of Teachers College, has devised a method which may save time and figures; it is especially convenient in that it helps to make clear the relative value of various foods for protein, calcium, phosphorus, and iron.

For this method, the 100-Calorie portions (with which you are already familiar through the weighing of 100-Calorie portions of foods, as outlined in Chapter II) serve as a basis. It will be recalled that by using these 100-Calorie portions it is easy to select the number of Calories needed by any one person or by a group of people. A selection of 30 portions of food, 100 Calories to a portion, will provide the energy for a person who needs 3000 Calories per day. Obviously, one 100-Calorie portion is 1/30 of the day's Calorie requirement for this person. If each 100-Calorie portion of food also contained 1/30 of the day's requirement of protein, calcium, phosphorus, and iron, food selection to meet the daily needs of any one person would be easy, but you must have noticed that very few foods are equally valuable for all foodstuffs. Eggs are high in protein and mineral elements; green vegetables contain very little protein but are rich in mineral elements and vitamins; while sugar contains neither protein nor mineral elements.

There must be another basis for judging the relative value of foods for these other food factors (protein, calcium, phosphorus, and iron). As a starting point for such comparisons, Mrs. Rose takes the average adult man, weighing 154 pounds. His daily food needs are as follows:

3000	Calories
75	grams of protein
0.67	gram of calcium
1.32	grams of phosphorus
0.015	gram of iron

In planning a diet for this average man, we naturally select 30 portions of food, each portion containing 100 Calories, to furnish the Calories needed. As previously stated, one 100-Calorie portion is 1/30 of his whole requirement and is called a share of the Calories needed during the day. For every 100 Calories of energy, this average man needs 1/30, or 1 share, of each of the other food requirements also, or:

1/30 of 75 grams of protein	2.5 grams
1/30 of 0.67 gram of calcium	0.023 gram
1/30 of 1.32 grams of phosphorus . . .	0.044 gram
1/30 of 0.015 gram of iron	0.0005 gram

For every 100 Calories, the average man must have 2.5 grams of protein, 0.023 gram of calcium, 0.044 gram of phosphorus, and 0.0005 gram of iron. Or, for every Calorie share, the average man needs one share of protein, one share of calcium, one share of phosphorus, and one share of iron. For his total requirement during the day, he needs 30 shares of each of the above foodstuffs.

A share of a man's requirement graphically repre-sented. Since one share of each food factor bears the same relation to the whole (each is 1/30 of the whole) as each of the others, they may be represented graphically by straight lines of the same length, as in Chart XX.

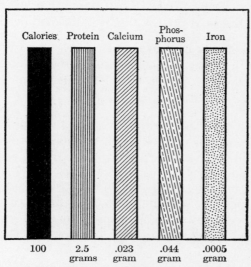

Calories	Protein	Calcium	Phos-phorus	Iron
100	2.5 grams	.023 gram	.044 gram	.0005 gram

Chart XX. — One share of a man's requirement for a day

How many shares of each food factor do you need? If a member of your family needs 1500 Calories, he or she will need 15 Calorie shares. An allowance of 15 per cent of the Calories from protein will provide 56 grams of protein. As each protein share has a value of 2.5 grams, the number of protein shares required for this girl or boy will be 22(56 ÷ 2.5). In the same way may be found the corresponding shares of calcium, phosphorus, and iron, with the following results:

Daily Requirement in Shares for a Girl or Boy Who Needs 1500 Calories

Requirement in grams		Requirement in shares
1500 Calories	÷ 100	= 15 shares
56 grams protein	÷ 2.5	= 22 shares
1 gram calcium	÷ 0.023	= 43 shares
1 gram phosphorus	÷ 0.044	= 23 shares
0.015 gram iron	÷ 0.0005	= 30 shares

Value of foods in shares. In Table XXVII will be found the number of shares of each food factor in 100 Calories of each common food. For instance, the share value of white potato is as follows:

Calories	1.0 share (100 Calories)
Protein	1.1 shares
Calcium	0.7 share
Phosphorus	1.6 shares
Iron	3.1 shares

If we let one large square on the graph paper represent the value of one share, we may draw a picture of the value of potatoes in shares as shown in Chart XXI. Interpreted in everyday language, we find that every 100-Calorie portion of potatoes (or one share) provides more than its share of protein and phosphorus; that it is a fair source of calcium, and a surprisingly good source of iron. In the same way we may find the number of shares of each food factor in white bread and represent them as in Chart XXII. Comparing these two charts, it is evident that the amount of white potato necessary to give 100 Calories provides much more calcium, phosphorus, and iron than does the same amount of white bread; in trying to raise the iron content of a diet, it would be much wiser, according to these two charts, to select white potato than white bread made with water.

If you make similar charts for each common food, you will have before you line drawings which will help to impress you with the relative value of the various foods for protein, calcium, phosphorus, and iron.

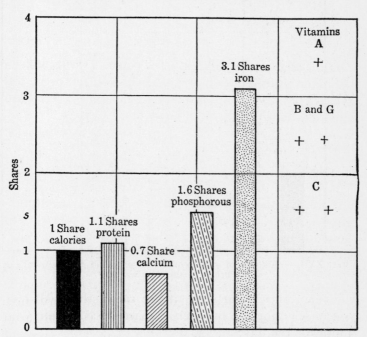

Chart XXI. — Amount of each food factor provided by one share of white potato [1]

If each separate foodstuff is given a different color (as red for Calories, blue for protein, yellow for calcium, orange for phosphorus, and green for iron), and if you

[1] This graphic method of representing the share value of foods is based on a plan used by Miss M. F. Eby, a teacher in the Home Economics Department of the Manual Arts High School, Los Angeles, California.

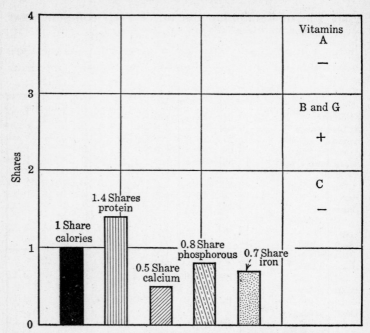

Chart XXII. — Amount of each food factor provided by one share of white bread (made with water) [1]

will place these charts about the room, they will help you in selecting the number of shares to complete your quota for the day.

Planning the diet by means of shares.   To plan your diet by means of shares, first determine the number of shares of Calories, protein, calcium, phosphorus, and iron required.   Then, by the aid of your food charts or by means of Table XXVII, compile your diet as in Method II.   Use Method I in selecting foods for your first plan.

[1] See footnote on page 137.

TABLE XXVII. — SHARE VALUE OF 100-CALORIE PORTIONS OF FOODS
(Copied from Rose's *Laboratory Handbook for Dietetics*, 1929
edition. Macmillan) Courtesy of Dr. M. S. Rose

FOOD MATERIAL (EDIBLE PART)	WEIGHT		CALO-RIES	PRO-TEIN	CAL-CIUM	PHOS-PHORUS	IRON
	Ounces	Grams	Shares	Shares	Shares	Shares	Shares
Almonds	0.54	15.5	1.0	1.29	1.61	1.64	1.20
Apples, fresh	5.61	159.0	1.0	0.26	0.52	0.45	0.96
Apricots, dried	1.27	36.0	1.0	0.68	1.03	0.93	1.01
Apricots, fresh	6.08	172.4	1.0	0.76	1.00	1.00	1.04
Asparagus, fresh	15.89	450.5	1.0	3.24	5.30	4.02	9.02
Avocado, West Indian	3.62	102.8	1.0	0.45	3.30	1.14	12.94
Bacon	0.56	16.0	1.0	0.67	0.04	0.41	0.42
Bananas	3.58	101.4	1.0	0.53	0.39	0.70	1.22
Beans, kidney, dried	1.01	28.8	1.0	2.33	1.74	3.25	4.32
Beans, Lima, dried	1.01	28.6	1.0	2.07	0.98	2.20	4.00
Beans, Lima, fresh	2.88	81.5	1.0	2.32	0.87	2.46	3.25
Beans, navy, dried	1.02	29.0	1.0	2.61	2.04	3.11	4.06
Beans, string, fresh	8.50	241.0	1.0	2.22	4.78	2.86	5.30
Beef, lean, round	2.26	64.0	1.0	5.45	0.37	3.32	3.08
Beets, fresh	7.66	217.1	1.0	1.39	2.78	1.91	2.60
Blackberries, fresh	6.10	173.0	1.0	0.90	1.26	1.32	2.08
Blueberries, fresh	4.76	135.0	1.0	0.32	1.17	0.25	2.40
Bluefish, fresh	3.99	113.1	1.0	8.78	1.03	5.73	2.49
Bread, Boston brown	1.56	44.2	1.0	0.96	2.44	1.86	2.60
Bread, graham or whole wheat (water) 100%	1.35	38.4	1.0	1.37	0.87	1.91	1.92
Bread, graham, 50%	1.36	38.7	1.0	1.40	0.66	1.37	1.22
Bread, rye	1.39	39.3	1.0	1.42	0.39	1.32	1.26
Bread, white (water)	1.38	39.0	1.0	1.44	0.48	0.82	0.70

TABLE XXVII (*Continued*)

FOOD MATERIAL (EDIBLE PART)	WEIGHT		CALORIES	PROTEIN	CALCIUM	PHOSPHORUS	IRON
	Ounces	Grams	Shares	Shares	Shares	Shares	Shares
Bread, white (milk)	1.26	35.7	1.0	1.41	0.98	0.79	0.58
Bread, whole wheat (milk) . . .	1.23	34.9	1.0	1.54	1.10	1.54	1.21
Brussels sprouts .	17.10	487.7	1.0	2.92	5.74	13.30	10.74
Butter . . .	0.46	13.0	1.0	0.05	0.09	0.05	0.06
Buttermilk . .	9.86	279.6	1.0	3.36	12.82	6.16	1.40
Cabbage . .	11.20	317.5	1.0	2.03	6.22	2.09	6.98
Cantaloupe . .	8.91	252.5	1.0	0.60	1.91	0.86	1.42
Carrots . . .	7.80	221.2	1.0	0.97	5.39	2.29	2.66
Cauliflower . .	11.57	327.9	1.0	2.36	17.52	4.54	3.94
Celery . . .	19.07	540.6	1.0	2.38	18.30	4.57	5.40
Chard . . .	9.23	263.2	1.0	3.35	17.09	2.38	13.16
Cheese, American .	0.80	22.8	1.0	2.60	9.22	3.54	0.60
Cherries, fresh .	4.52	128.2	1.0	0.48	1.09	0.88	1.02
Chestnuts, fresh .	1.46	41.3	1.0	1.02	0.61	1.00	0.58
Chicken, broilers .	3.27	92.6	1.0	7.96	0.52	4.88	6.30
Chocolate, unsweetened .	0.58	16.4	1.0	0.84	0.65	1.71	0.88
Clams, long . .	6.86	194.6	1.0	6.70	12.39	6.41	19.40
Clams, round . .	7.61	215.5	1.0	5.60	9.96	2.27	19.40
Cocoa, powder . .	0.71	20.1	1.0	1.74	1.00	3.25	1.08
Coconut, fresh . .	0.60	16.9	1.0	0.38	0.17	0.30	0.60
Cod steak . . .	4.49	126.6	1.0	9.47	1.12	6.19	2.53
Corn, green . . .	3.49	99.0	1.0	1.22	0.26	2.31	1.58
Cornmeal . . .	0.99	28.1	1.0	1.04	0.22	1.20	0.60
Crackers, soda . .	0.85	24.2	1.0	0.95	0.26	0.57	0.72
Cranberries, fresh .	7.57	214.6	1.0	0.34	1.70	0.61	2.58
Cream, 18% fat .	1.81	51.4	1.0	0.51	2.17	1.00	0.20
Cream, 40% fat .	0.93	26.3	1.0	0.23	0.87	0.45	0.10
Cucumbers . . .	20.28	574.8	1.0	1.84	3.91	4.34	2.30
Currants, dried . .	1.10	31.1	1.0	0.30	1.13	1.39	1.74
Currants, fresh . .	6.17	174.8	1.0	1.05	1.96	1.50	1.74
Dandelion greens .	5.78	163.9	1.0	1.57	7.48	2.66	8.80
Dates, dried . .	1.02	28.8	1.0	0.24	0.83	0.36	1.72
Duck, breast . .	2.96	83.9	1.0	7.48	0.47	4.58	5.54
Eggplant . . .	12.64	358.4	1.0	1.72	1.78	2.77	3.68
Eggs	2.38	67.5	1.0	3.62	1.96	2.77	4.10

TABLE XXVII (*Continued*)

Food Material (edible part)	Weight		Calories	Protein	Calcium	Phosphorus	Iron
	Ounces	Grams	Shares	Shares	Shares	Shares	Shares
Egg white . . .	6.92	196.1	1.0	9.65	0.87	0.50	0.40
Egg yolk . . .	0.97	27.6	1.0	1.73	1.56	3.30	4.60
Endive	25.10	714.3	1.0	2.86	32.29	20.29	11.43
Farina, dark . .	0.97	27.6	1.0	1.23	0.57	2.68	2.80
Farina, light . .	0.97	27.6	1.0	1.22	0.26	0.80	0.44
Figs, dried . . .	1.12	31.6	1.0	0.54	2.21	0.84	1.90
Filberts	0.50	14.2	1.0	0.90	1.78	1.14	1.14
Flour, buckwheat .	1.01	28.7	1.0	0.74	0.48	1.48	0.68
Flour, whole wheat	0.98	27.8	1.0	1.54	0.39	1.50	1.40
Flour, graham . .	0.98	27.9	1.0	1.48	0.48	2.29	2.00
Flour, white (wheat) . .	1.00	28.3	1.0	1.28	0.26	0.59	0.46
Flour, rye . . .	1.01	28.5	1.0	0.78	0.22	1.86	0.74
Goose, young . .	0.90	25.6	1.0	1.67	0.10	1.02	1.22
Grapefruit . . .	7.45	212.8	1.0	0.46	1.73	0.82	1.16
Grape juice . . .	3.53	100.0	1.0	. . .	0.48	0.25	0.60
Grapes	3.66	103.7	1.0	0.54	0.83	0.73	0.62
Haddock, fresh . .	4.94	139.9	1.0	9.62	1.16	6.26	2.52
Halibut steak . .	2.93	82.5	1.0	6.14	0.72	4.02	1.68
Ham, lean, smoked	1.32	37.5	1.0	2.97	0.19	2.02	2.20
Herring, fresh . .	2.49	70.5	1.0	5.50	0.64	2.57	1.51
Herring, smoked .	1.22	34.5	1.0	5.09	0.64	2.57	1.51
Hominy	1.00	28.3	1.0	0.93	0.09	0.61	0.50
Honey	1.08	30.6	1.0	0.05	0.09	0.14	0.60
Kale	6.92	196.1	1.0	2.67	18.07	2.67	12.16
Kidney, veal . .	2.82	79.9	1.0	5.40	0.34	3.31	6.55
Kohl-rabi . . .	11.33	323.6	1.0	2.59	10.83	4.23	3.88
Lamb, breast . .	1.22	34.6	1.0	2.64	0.18	1.65	2.00
Lamb chop, broiled	0.99	28.1	1.0	2.52	0.15	1.60	1.83
Lamb, leg, medium fat	1.57	44.4	1.0	3.41	0.21	2.09	1.33
Lemons . . .	7.96	225.7	1.0	0.90	3.52	1.11	2.70
Lentils, dried . .	1.01	28.7	1.0	2.95	1.35	2.86	4.94
Lettuce . . .	18.47	523.6	1.0	2.51	9.74	5.09	7.34
Liver, beef . . .	2.73	77.6	1.0	6.33	0.60	3.88	12.57
Macaroni . . .	0.99	28.0	1.0	1.48	0.26	0.91	0.66
Mackerel, fresh .	2.54	72.1	1.0	5.39	0.63	3.52	1.44

Table XXVII (*Continued*)

Food Material (edible part)	Weight		Calo-ries	Pro-tein	Cal-cium	Phos-phorus	Iron
	Ounces	Grams	Shares	Shares	Shares	Shares	Shares
Maple syrup . .	1.23	35.0	1.0	. . .	1.61	0.07	2.00
Milk, condensed, sweetened . .	1.08	30.6	1.0	1.08	4.18	1.64	0.40
Milk, condensed (evaporated) . .	2.11	59.9	1.0	2.30	8.22	3.32	0.80
Milk, skimmed . .	9.61	272.5	1.0	3.70	14.39	5.95	1.36
Milk, whole . . .	5.10	144.5	1.0	1.90	7.56	3.05	0.70
Molasses, cane . .	1.23	34.9	1.0	0.33	3.22	0.34	5.10
Mushrooms . . .	7.86	223.2	1.0	3.12	1.65	5.48	. . .
Muskmelons . .	8.91	252.5	1.0	0.60	1.87	0.86	1.60
Mustard greens .	11.49	325.7	1.0	3.26	31.17	4.89	36.48
Mutton, leg, lean	1.85	52.4	1.0	4.15	0.28	2.54	3.12
Oats, rolled . . .	0.89	25.2	1.0	1.68	0.74	2.25	1.92
Olives, green . .	1.18	33.4	1.0	0.15	1.78	0.09	1.94
Onions	7.24	205.4	1.0	1.32	3.00	2.11	2.00
Oranges	6.86	194.6	1.0	0.62	3.83	0.91	0.78
Orange juice . .	8.17	231.5	1.0	. . .	2.91	0.84	0.92
Oysters	7.00	198.4	1.0	4.92	4.61	6.95	17.86
Parsnips . . .	5.43	154.1	1.0	0.99	3.96	2.66	1.80
Peaches, fresh .	8.53	242.1	1.0	0.68	1.65	1.30	1.46
Peanuts . . .	0.64	18.2	1.0	1.88	0.57	1.66	0.72
Pears, fresh . .	5.57	158.0	1.0	0.38	1.04	0.93	0.94
Peas, dried . .	0.99	28.1	1.0	2.77	1.03	2.57	3.23
Peas, green . .	3.52	99.9	1.0	2.77	1.13	2.90	3.30
Pecans	0.48	13.6	1.0	0.52	0.52	1.02	0.70
Peppers, green .	13.54	386.1	1.0	1.84	1.00	2.27	3.08
Pigeon	3.83	108.5	1.0	9.89	0.61	6.07	7.38
Pineapple, fresh	8.18	232.0	1.0	0.37	1.78	1.45	2.32
Plums, fresh . .	4.18	118.5	1.0	0.48	1.04	0.86	1.18
Pork, loin chop, lean	1.40	39.7	1.0	3.22	0.20	1.97	1.20
Potato, sweet .	2.86	81.2	1.0	0.58	0.69	0.84	0.82
Potato, white . .	4.23	120.0	1.0	1.06	0.69	1.57	3.12
Prunes, dried . .	1.17	33.2	1.0	0.28	0.78	0.80	2.00
Pumpkin, fresh .	13.72	389.1	1.0	1.56	3.87	5.20	2.60
Quail	2.19	62.0	1.0	6.20	0.40	3.80	4.71
Radishes . .	12.04	341.3	1.0	1.77	3.17	2.23	4.10
Raisins	1.02	29.0	1.0	0.30	0.83	0.86	1.22

Table XXVII (*Continued*)

Food Material (edible part)	Weight		Calories	Protein	Calcium	Phosphorus	Iron
	Ounces	Grams	Shares	Shares	Shares	Shares	Shares
Raspberries, fresh .	5.33	151.1	1.0	1.03	3.22	1.77	1.82
Rhubarb, fresh . .	15.27	433.0	1.0	1.04	8.22	3.05	8.66
Rice, brown . .	1.01	28.5	1.0	1.01	0.14	1.36	1.16
Rice, white . .	1.01	28.5	1.0	0.91	0.04	0.61	0.52
Rutabagas . . .	8.60	243.9	1.0	1.26	8.04	3.18	2.55
Salmon, fresh . .	1.75	49.2	1.0	4.33	0.49	2.82	1.19
Sardines, canned .	1.31	37.1	1.0	3.42	0.56	3.09	1.31
Shad	2.19	62.2	1.0	4.68	0.54	3.05	1.24
Shredded wheat .	0.97	27.4	1.0	1.40	0.48	2.02	2.46
Smelts . . .	4.07	115.5	1.0	8.13	0.95	5.30	2.31
Spinach . . .	14.76	418.4	1.0	3.51	12.22	6.48	30.12
Squab . . .	1.29	36.6	1.0	7.22	0.18	1.67	2.05
Squash, summer .	13.64	389.1	1.0	1.55	3.00	1.41	4.60
Squash, winter .	7.67	217.4	1.0	1.22	1.74	1.39	2.60
Strawberries, fresh .	9.04	256.4	1.0	1.02	4.55	1.64	4.10
Tapioca . . .	0.99	28.2	1.0	0.04	0.18	0.57	0.90
Tomatoes, canned .	15.63	442.5	1.0	1.58	2.17	2.57	3.50
Tuna fish, canned without oil . .	2.85	80.9	1.0	7.02	0.82	4.56	1.94
Tuna fish, canned in oil . . .	1.27	35.9	1.0	3.65	0.44	2.38	1.01
Turkey meat, dark, cooked . .	1.81	51.2	1.0	8.02	0.51	4.91	6.04
Turkey meat, light, cooked . .	1.93	54.8	1.0	7.58	0.48	4.65	5.70
Turnip greens . .	11.99	340.1	1.0	3.67	45.56	4.25	44.90
Turnips . . .	8.95	253.8	1.0	1.32	7.00	2.66	2.55
Veal, lean, breast .	2.25	63.8	1.0	5.40	0.37	3.24	3.92
Veal, lean, leg .	2.89	81.9	1.0	6.98	0.44	4.28	4.26
Walnuts, California	0.50	14.2	1.0	1.04	0.56	1.14	0.60
Watermelon . .	11.68	331.1	1.0	0.53	1.65	0.23	1.98

PROBLEMS

47. To find your own food requirement by the share method:
    What is your Calorie requirement? How many shares does
    this represent?

How many shares of protein will you need if you allow 30 grams of protein for each 1000 Calories?

How many shares of calcium will you need to supply your one gram of calcium daily?

How many shares of phosphorus will you need to supply your one gram of phosphorus daily?

How many shares of iron will you need daily if you allow 0.005 gram of iron for each 1000 Calories?

48. Arrange a day's meals for yourself, using the 100-Calorie portions, which will meet your Calorie requirement.

Check the number of shares of protein supplied by the food.

Check the number of shares of calcium, of phosphorus, and of iron supplied by the food. (Use Table XXVII)

Are the protein, calcium, phosphorus, and iron adequate?

Are the foods valuable for vitamins sufficiently represented?

If your diet, as planned, does not meet your requirement in shares, as determined above, rearrange until it is satisfactory.

49. Using Chart XXI as a guide, make a chart for each of the following foods to show the number of shares of protein, calcium, phosphorus, and iron supplied by each food· also represent the vitamin values:

One glass of milk	160 Calories
One egg	70 Calories
Four prunes.	100 Calories
One third cup of oatmeal (uncooked) . .	100 Calories
One large orange	100 Calories

QUESTIONS

1. What methods are suggested in this chapter for the selection of foods?

2. Which one do you consider would be most practical for your own use in planning meals in your home?

3. Explain the share method of calculating food values.

4. What do you consider are some of the advantages of the share method?

5. Completion test:

   Every diet should contain foods which supply ——, ——, ——, ——, ——, and ——.

   If a man needs 3000 Calories, he must have —— portions of food, each of which is called a ——, and each of which furnishes —— Calories.

   This same man needs —— grams of protein for each —— Calories.

   A share of calcium in his diet is equal to —— gram.

   A share of iron in his diet is equal to —— gram.

REFERENCES

For students:

ROSE, MARY S. *Foundations of Nutrition*, Chapter II. The Macmillan Company (1927).

For teachers:

ROSE, MARY S. *Foundations of Nutrition*, Chapter II; Chapter XII, pages 374 to 387. The Macmillan Company (1927).

A real little girl who was fed according to the schedule prepared for Baby Betty

CHAPTER VIII

FEEDING THE IRVING FAMILY — LUNCHEONS FOR A HIGH-SCHOOL BOY OR GIRL

Boys and girls between the ages of twelve and sixteen years need more food in proportion to weight than at any later time in life. During this adolescent period, food must provide for unusual activity, for unusual growth, and for the maintenance of from eighty to one hundred and twenty pounds of tissues already grown. That huge appetite of boys and girls is nature's way of helping them to satisfy their needs. In addition to food, there should be long hours of sleep, with some exercise in the open air each day.

THE IRVING FAMILY

Its makeup and characteristics. Mrs. Irving, like many another mother, had to plan meals for a large family, consisting of six children, grandmother Irving, Mr. Irving, and herself. There was baby Betty who was a year old. Betty was the pet of the household, good-natured, and a joy when some one was with her, but most unhappy when not receiving attention. As a result she was frequently given something to eat to keep her quiet. She was restless and easily disturbed when asleep, but otherwise apparently healthy.

Jack, who was three years old, was a bright, keen boy, active, excitable, and always too busy to take a nap.

He bolted his food at mealtime so as to get back to his rocking horse or his ball, and was frequently seen eating sweet cakes and fruit between meals.   Although usually healthy, he frequently had a cold that kept him from gaining as he should.

Dick was seven years old and thin for his age.   He was fond of reading and was often allowed to sit up late at night to finish a story.   He drank coffee, seldom touched milk, preferred his eggs fried, almost never touched vegetables, but was very fond of meat, white bread, sweets, and sweet desserts.   Mrs. Irving often wondered why he was so pale and thin, as he had been a perfect specimen of health when he was Jack's age.

Clare was ten years old, the strongest and healthiest member of the family.   She had rosy cheeks and sparkling eyes, was wide awake, and always well and happy. Although she was extremely fond of having a good time, she applied herself diligently to her lessons, mastered them in a short time, and was off to her play.   She was busy all day long, but she was ready for bed by nine o'clock and slept soundly until morning.   She had a splendid appetite, she loved milk, she ate plenty of bread, cereals, vegetables, and fruit, but she was not very fond of meat and often ate none at all.   Neither did she care for sweets and she seldom ate between meals.

Alice and Tom Irving were in the last half of the sophomore year in high school.   For two years Alice, who was only fourteen years of age and an extremely bright student, had been the leader of her class as well as a leader of social activities, but of late her records had not been up to standard and she was always too tired to enter into any of the social functions at school.

She was thin, for she was trying to keep a slender figure; she tired easily; and she was losing her charm and vivacity of manner. Because her marks had been below their usual high grade, every minute of the afternoon was devoted to the preparation of her lessons for the next day, but while she spent several hours more in study than formerly, she did not seem to accomplish as much as before.

Tom was one year older than Alice and of average weight for his height and age, for he had a never-ceasing appetite and he enjoyed his food; in fact, his mother was afraid he ate too much and often remonstrated with him. It did not worry him if he did not stand as high in his class work as Alice, but there was a sting in the taunts of his friends to the effect that he could no longer outdistance the rest of the boys in his gymnasium record. Being a good sport, he laughed good-naturedly at their remarks and pretended not to mind, but inwardly he decided to find out why he was losing ground.

He had heard that a cousin of his, who was a college athlete, had to observe certain food and other health habits, so he quietly began a bit of investigation. First he consulted the physical education director who suggested that he go to his doctor for a physical examination. The doctor told him that there was nothing physically wrong with him, but that he was growing rapidly and needed plenty of nourishing food. As he was eating incessantly, Tom did not see how food could have anything to do with his lack of pep, and at first he was inclined to laugh at the idea and think no more about it; then he decided to confide in his mother who was always interested in the plans and problems of her children and ready to do anything within her power. She readily agreed to help Tom solve his difficulty.

The doctor's advice. The relation of food to health was a new idea to Mrs. Irving, but her confidence in her family physician led her to discuss with him Tom's lack of strength and Alice's fatigue and loss of weight. He showed her some graphs like Charts I, II, III, and IV in this book and explained that the great increase in weight which takes place from twelve to sixteen years as there represented indicates why a large amount of food is necessary during adolescence. An enormous appetite is not a cause for alarm but rather an aid in providing sufficient food to take care of the increase in weight and to build up a good, healthy physique. If ample food is not provided, proper growth is interfered with and boys and girls can never develop into the kind of men and women they will later wish to be. Moreover, they will be more susceptible to diseases, especially tuberculosis.

While there is little danger of too much of the right kind of food, much harm may result from the eating of too much food that provides chiefly fuel energy without the strength-giving qualities. The doctor said that Tom might possibly need 4500 Calories a day during his training for the athletic contest or when otherwise exercising vigorously, but that his food should be such as to make strong muscles as well as fatty tissue and energy. The doctor also emphasized the need for eight to ten hours of sleep each night to give the tissues a chance to make use of the food eaten. He then gave Mrs. Irving the names of several books which he said would help her.

POSTURE STANDARDS
Intermediate-Type Boys

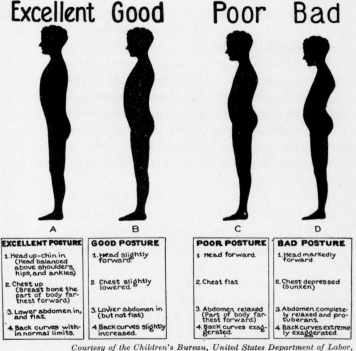

Excellent   Good   Poor   Bad

A   B   C   D

EXCELLENT POSTURE	GOOD POSTURE	POOR POSTURE	BAD POSTURE
1. Head up–chin in (Head balanced above shoulders, hips, and ankles)	1. Head slightly forward.	1 Head forward.	1. Head markedly forward.
2. Chest up (Breast bone the part of body farthest forward.)	2 Chest slightly lowered.	2. Chest flat	2. Chest depressed (sunken)
3. Lower abdomen in, and flat.	3. Lower abdomen in (but not flat)	3. Abdomen relaxed (Part of body farthest forward.)	3. Abdomen completely relaxed and protuberant.
4. Back curves within normal limits.	4. Back curves slightly increased.	4. Back curves exaggerated.	4. Back curves extremely exaggerated.

Courtesy of the Children's Bureau, United States Department of Labor,
Washington, D. C.

Illustration No. 7. — Good posture improves health and personal
appearance. Although the pictures above illustrate good posture
for boys, the line of head, shoulders, hips, and feet is the same for
girls

Meals for Alice and Tom

What the books said. Alice, Tom, and Mrs. Irving studied the books very carefully. In them they found the very same things that Chapters I to VI of this book have been telling us; namely, that tissues are built from foods eaten, and that the strength and endurance in the tissues, the kind of work the tissues are able to do, and their ability to withstand fatigue and disease are strongly influenced by the kind and amount of protein, mineral elements, and vitamins, and the number of Calories in the food. They learned that the best combination of foods to provide these foodstuffs is from one pint to one quart of milk daily, generous servings of two or more vegetables every day (of which one should be a green leafy vegetable), some citrus fruit or tomatoes, one serving of a protein food in addition to milk, and plenty of energy food.

The value of the meals of Alice and Tom. In their interest in their own food, Alice and Tom recorded their meals for a day, and this is what they saw:

Alice	Tom

Breakfast

Alice	Tom
Orange	Orange
Roll (1) Butter ($\frac{1}{2}$ oz.)	Cornflakes (1 c.) Cream ($\frac{1}{4}$c.)
Egg (1)	Rolls (4) Butter (2 oz.)
Coffee with 2 tbsp. cream and 2 tsp. sugar	Eggs (3) Bacon (4 slices)
	Coffee with 2 tbsp. cream and 2 tsp. sugar

Luncheon

Alice	Tom
Ice cream ($\frac{1}{4}$ c.)	Ice cream (1 c.)
Cake (1)	Cakes (4)
Pickles	Bananas (2 to 3)

Afternoon Luncheon

Cake (1)   Frankfurter sandwich
Candy (4 to 5 pieces)   Apples
Apple (1)

Dinner

Meat (3 oz.)   Meat (6 oz.)
Potato (1 small)   Potatoes (2 to 3)
Tomatoes (1)   Bread (4 slices)
Apple tapioca ($\frac{1}{2}$ c.)   Butter (2 oz.)
                                        Tomatoes (2)
                                        Apple tapioca (1 c.)

Alice and Tom were somewhat surprised when they realized how essential is milk and how little of it each had received. "Do you suppose we have had enough calcium?" they asked, and Tom remarked that he believed his gymnastic record had begun to fall off about the same time or soon after he stopped drinking milk. They were dismayed also at the complete absence of green leafy vegetables, in fact, at the scarcity of vegetables in general, and they wondered whether or not they were having the correct amount of iron and other food substances. Their curiosity about these various points led them to calculate the food value of these three meals, with results as follows:

	CALORIES	PROTEIN	CALCIUM	PHOSPHORUS	IRON
		Grams	Grams	Grams	Grams
Tom . .	4500	120	0.65	1.63	0.022
Alice . .	1475	36	0.25	0.53	0.007

A comparison of the actual with the desirable. Naturally, Alice and Tom were still more curious to compare these food values with what would be con-

sidered an adequate diet for each of them; and, again
consulting the books, they found that, if the average
weight of a girl as old as Alice is 90 pounds and of a boy
the age of Tom is 120 pounds, each requires approximately:

	CALORIES	PROTEIN	CALCIUM	PHOSPHORUS	IRON
		Grams	Grams	Grams	Grams
Tom .	Up to 4500 [1]	90[2]	1.0	1.0	0.015
Alice .	2200	66[2]	1.0	1.0	0.011

[1] Since it is probable that the need for protein and mineral elements does
not increase in proportion to the energy requirement after a Calorie requirement of 3000 Calories has been reached, Tom's protein and iron are calculated on the basis of 3000 Calories.

[2] Protein is calculated on the basis of 30 grams per 1000 Calories.

A study of these figures shows very clearly that in-
stinct does not protect a person from an inadequate
diet. While Tom's food, which was freely chosen,
supplied sufficient energy, protein, phosphorus, iron,
and doubtless most other mineral elements, it was low
in calcium. The lack of vegetables, with no dark
bread or cereal, would indicate, also, a deficiency of at
least vitamins A, B, and G. A calcium deficiency alone
is enough to prevent maximum physical efficiency, but
with both low calcium and insufficient vitamins, Tom
was in danger of losing more than an athletic record.
Mrs. Irving felt they were fortunate indeed to have
discovered these errors in his diet in time to prevent
more serious results, but Tom's chief delight was cen-
tered in his renewed confidence in regaining his former
athletic standing; he was also interested because he
had read that diet has much to do with the skin eruption

with which many boys of his age are afflicted, and now, realizing that it might be caused by too much fat and too rich food, he was sure he could control it.

Alice had been eating too little food in general, so that her Calories were low as well as her protein, mineral elements, and vitamins. She had been satisfying her appetite with sweets and starchy foods — foods which are not only low in calcium, iron, iodine, and vitamins, but which dull the appetite for the foods that provide these health essentials. Now that Alice had found at least one cause for her loss of vitality and her inability to concentrate, and one which she could remedy easily, she too began to feel very hopeful of better things for the future.

PROBLEMS

50. Reconstruct the meals of Alice and Tom as given on page 152, so as to meet their food requirements. Increase Calories, protein, calcium, phosphorus, and iron for Alice. Increase calcium for Tom and include more foods rich in vitamins for both Alice and Tom. Make a record of the corrected meals in your notebook.

51. Determine the number of shares of Calories, protein, calcium, phosphorus, and iron contributed by the corrected meals for Alice and Tom as worked out in Problem 50.

Three substantial meals a day. As Mrs. Irving studied her problem still more, she realized that she had been trying to make her meals appetizing by preparing almost exclusively the things the children liked best, but in her mistaken kindness she had been undermining their health by entirely neglecting food values. She found that her family of growing boys and girls needed three **substantial** as well as attractive meals each day.

Breakfast should contain about one third of the growing material for the day with enough energy to last until noontime, thereby preventing the burning of the body tissue for this purpose. Likewise, the luncheon must consist of nourishing as well as satisfying foods to forestall the desire for constant nibbling during the afternoon, a practice which destroys the appetite for the evening meal. The evening meal, the heartiest meal of the day, presents an opportunity to include all the food requirements for growth which it has not been possible to give in the morning and noon meals.

Mid-afternoon luncheons. With a hearty noonday meal, a mid-afternoon luncheon is usually considered unwise, but during these years of rapid growth and unusual activity, if time does not permit the eating of a hearty meal at noon, a light luncheon about three o'clock is sometimes desirable. When given, the mid-afternoon luncheon should be carefully planned, and eaten at the same time each day, at least three hours before the next meal. It should by no means be a complete meal; neither should it be sweets of any kind. A glass of milk, graham crackers and milk, a piece of whole wheat bread and butter, or a piece of fruit is sufficient in case this extra meal is advised.

The problem of the noonday meal. Alice and Tom had their breakfasts and dinners with the rest of the family, so that no extra arrangements for them were necessary at these times; but Mrs. Irving was puzzled to know what was best for their luncheon. They lived some distance from the high school, and, as it had not seemed wise for them to spend the time coming from and returning to school during their brief intermission, they had been buying their lunches wherever they liked. Mrs. Irving had been trying to coax Alice to eat heartily by giving her an extra allowance with which to buy anything that appealed to her; Alice had been buying ice cream cones, cakes, fruit, sweet chocolate, candy, and the like, any one of which would make a good ending for a hearty meal, but none of which contained any great amount of the health regulators which Alice so much needed. There was abundant evidence that these foods had not satisfied the demands of the tissues, for after school Alice was tired, irritable, and hungry. She tried to obtain relief by eating more fruit and candy, but the chief result was a spoiled appetite for dinner. A continued practice of purchasing the luncheons from the corner store, the confectioner's, or the ice cream counter is almost sure to rob the cheeks and lips of their color, the eyes of their sparkle, and the manner of its enthusiasm, as it had been doing in Alice's case.

The home-cooked luncheon is best. Fortunate is the boy or girl who has time in which to go home at noon where he may sit quietly and eat slowly a very nourishing meal, with milk and vegetables as its foundation. A simple, one-dish meal, with plenty of time in which to eat and return to school, is much more healthful than a more elaborate meal hurriedly eaten. Many interesting combinations may be planned with mashed or chopped vegetables, meat, and fish, in soups, stews, purées, chowders, salads, or meat pies; with milk, scrambled eggs, baked beans, macaroni (or rice) and cheese, or cereals thoroughly cooked and served with milk, cream, or butter, or in cereal puddings. The shorter the time in which to eat the meal, the more essential it is to have it planned to contain concentrated nourishment which may be eaten in a minimum of time. This means that the foods which need chewing, and which should be included daily for the sake of the teeth, must be omitted at this meal.

Cost versus food value. The cost of a luncheon is no indication of its food value. The two luncheons given in Problem 52 show the comparison between cost and labor on the one hand, and food value and ease of eating on the other.

PROBLEM

52. To prepare a suitable noonday meal to be eaten at home:

Menus

(a) Creamed potatoes   1 c. combined with 0.8 oz. cheese
Whole wheat bread 3 oz.
Butter $\frac{1}{2}$ oz.
Baked apple
Cocoa made entirely with milk

(b) Tomato bisque $\frac{3}{4}$ c.
Broiled fish   3 oz.
Lettuce   1 oz.
Oil   1 tbsp.
Whole wheat bread 1$\frac{1}{2}$ oz.
Butter $\frac{1}{2}$ oz.
Sliced banana   1
Top milk $\frac{1}{4}$ c.

Prepare these luncheons; calculate the protein, phosphorus, calcium, iron, energy, and cost of each. Record, in tabulated form, the results from the two luncheons in your notebook.

Compare the two luncheons as to food value and cost.

Is the food value suited to the needs of a school girl 15 years of age?

The school lunch counter. A home-cooked luncheon is to be preferred if boys and girls have time in which to eat properly; but when they live so far from school that they have to hurry home, swallow food only half chewed, or eat only half enough, and then hurry back to school, perhaps worrying for fear of being late, they ought not to go home.   Such was the decision for Alice and Tom, but they and their mother decided that, since a home luncheon was impossible, it would be better for them to buy their luncheons at the school lunch counter in the future rather than from the street corners as previously.   They talked it over together and came to the following agreement:

1.   Alice decided that her luncheon should contain from 500 to 700 Calories; Tom thought he would need at least 800 to 1000 Calories if he were to have a total Calorie intake of 4500 Calories for the day.

2.   Each should select **nourishing** luncheons containing, so far as possible, such dishes as milk and vegetable soups, chowders, and purées, vegetable plates or salads, escalloped vegetables, cheese or vegetable sandwiches, baked beans, milk, and milk and cereal or egg desserts.   Some satisfactory combinations which they worked out were:

  (*a*) A hot milk and vegetable soup
       Two lettuce or tomato sandwiches (three or four for Tom)
       Ice cream or custard
       Iced cake for Tom

(b) Two jelly and peanut butter sandwiches (four for Tom)
Glass of milk
Rice or tapioca pudding
Banana for Tom

(c) Baked beans with brown bread (four slices of bread for Tom)
Carrots
Glass of milk
Baked apple with cream

(d) Vegetable plate
Whole wheat bread and butter (four slices for Tom)
Cocoa made with milk
Fruit jelly with whipped cream
Gingerbread (two pieces for Tom)

(e) Corn chowder with pilot crackers (four crackers for Tom)
Fruit salad with cheese straws
Ice cream and cookies (four cookies for Tom)

(f) Macaroni and cheese
Whole wheat bread and butter (four slices for Tom)
Vegetable salad
Glass of milk
Chocolate cake

3. There should be only one sweet at a meal; for example, jelly sandwiches, iced cake, frosted cookies, sweet chocolate; candy was to be permitted only once a week.

4. In making their selections they were to consider the food needs of the whole day. If they had eggs for breakfast, they would not select eggs for luncheon; if they had citrus fruit for breakfast, it would be better for them to select dessert with more Calories for luncheon; if they had only three glasses of milk at home, they were to drink the fourth glass at noon. Since

Mrs. Irving almost always planned to have meat at night, they were to have no meat at the noon meal.

5. They agreed that thin soups and cocoa in the same meal are a poor combination as they give a feeling of fullness without supplying enough material for growth and energy.

6. They agreed to avoid doughnuts, fried foods, sausages, rich pastries, coffee, tea, and cocoa made with water.

PROBLEM

53. To select a luncheon from the school menu:[1]

Menu

Bean soup (made with milk)
Vegetable soup (made with water)
Lamb stew
Fish hash
Cocoa
Milk
Ham sandwiches
Peanut butter sandwiches
Cake
Baked apple
Fresh fruit

Select luncheons for the following people:

(a) For a girl who has brought plain bread and butter sandwiches from home
(b) For a girl who has brought fruit from home
(c) For a girl who has brought such a light luncheon that it does not satisfy her
(d) For a girl who has brought no luncheon
(e) For a boy who has brought no luncheon

If possible, use your actual school menu, from which the students may select their luncheons; have the prepared foods if possible.

The box luncheon. The box or basket luncheon is a difficult problem; but sometimes boys and girls and men and women are so situated that it seems the only means of serving a substantial meal. It may be inconvenient to prepare and to carry, but, if the trouble it takes spells HEALTH, it is worth while. A box luncheon should be inviting enough to tempt the fickle appetite of growing girls, and ample enough to satisfy the huge appetite of growing boys. If the luncheon really satisfies, there will be less of that craving for sweets which is the cause of many illnesses.

The average luncheon should contain from 500 to 700 Calories (more, for a boy like Tom) of such foods as will provide a well-proportioned amount of the various foodstuffs, but its make-up will depend somewhat on the other two meals of the day. The most satisfying combinations are sandwiches, simple desserts, a bottle of milk, and some fruit.

The maximum amount of nourishment may be furnished in sandwiches made of whole wheat, oatmeal, brown, raisin, or nut bread. They may be plain bread-and-butter sandwiches, or the food value may be increased by a filling of eggs, peanut butter, chopped meat, baked beans, cheese (plain, or combined with dried fruit, jam or jelly, or chopped green vegetables), or a combination of nuts and dried fruits, such as raisins, figs, or dates. By referring to Tables XXII, XXIII, XXIV, XXV, and XXVI, it will be noticed that most of the foods mentioned are those richest in either protein or iron, or both. A bottle of milk should be included, either as a beverage or in some cooked form.

Simple desserts are to be preferred, such as crisp

ginger cookies, date or nut cookies, and plain cake, such as molasses, sponge, or cup cake. A bar of sweet chocolate is often permissible and gives variety to a box luncheon. If fruit is not included in the filling of the sandwiches, and if it fits in well with the other two meals of the day, it may be supplied by some fresh fruit, or by a jar of stewed fruit, or by a few dates or raisins; the dates may be given plain or they may be stuffed with peanut butter or cream cheese if desired. If it is not convenient to carry a bottle of milk, the milk may be made into custard, or into cornstarch or tapioca pudding. These may be carried in a jar with a screw top or in a paper carton.

PROBLEMS

54. Plan and pack a luncheon of 700 Calories. The luncheon should consist of sandwiches, fruit, and a sweet dessert.

55. Plan and pack (for a girl 15 years of age) a luncheon that will contain at least one third of the iron and protein needed for the day, and that can be packed in small space.

56. Suggest five box luncheons that will be well-balanced, inexpensive, and at the same time attractive. (If you carry your luncheon to school, try your menus for the coming week.)
    Note. Wash all fruit before putting it in the lunch box. When packing a luncheon, wrap each article in waxed paper. Line the box with a paper napkin. Pack the food carefully. Paper drinking cups may be used to hold salads and soft desserts. Fold a napkin neatly over the top. Use fresh clean paper when wrapping the box, and tie securely with clean, strong string.

QUESTIONS

1. If we are to study the needs of the Irving family, we must make their acquaintance. Of whom does the family consist? Which ones are being considered in this chapter?

2. What do you consider was the cause of Alice's fatigue and her falling below standard in her class work?

3. What ambitions had Tom, and why was he losing ground?

4. Mrs. Irving consulted the family doctor. What did he say about the food needs of Alice and Tom?

5. What mistakes had Mrs. Irving been making? What advice could you have given her?

6. What were some of the things the Irvings learned about their diet from the books the doctor recommended?

7. When boys and girls are in high school, the noon luncheon is nearly always a problem. How have you solved it for yourself?

8. Completion test:

Alice Irving found that her meals were lacking in ——, ——, ——,——, and ——.

Tom Irving found that his meals were lacking in —— and ——.

Alice and Tom decided they both needed —— to supply the ——.

Alice and Tom decided they both needed more —— —— to supply more ——.

REFERENCES

For students:

HARRIS, J. W. and LACEY, E. V. *Everyday Foods*, Chapters XIII and XIV. Houghton Mifflin Company (1927).

ROSE, MARY S. *Feeding the Family*, third edition, Chapter X, pages 194 to 205. The Macmillan Company (1929).

For teachers:

HUNT, C. L. "Good Proportions in the Diet," *Farmers' Bulletin No. 1313*. U. S. Department of Agriculture, Washington, D. C.

HUNT, C. L. "School Lunches," *Farmers' Bulletin No. 712*. U. S. Department of Agriculture, Washington, D. C.

ROSE, MARY S. *Foundations of Nutrition*, Chapter XII, pages 415 to 428. The Macmillan Company (1927).

SHERMAN, H. C. *Chemistry of Food and Nutrition*, third edition, Chapter XIX. The Macmillan Company (1926).

CHAPTER IX

FOOD FOR THE BABY

MOTHER'S milk is the best food for a normal baby, but gradually throughout the first year there should be added cod-liver oil, orange or tomato juice, vegetable water, vegetable pulp, egg yolk, and strained cereals. These foods help to make the child stronger, his bones better developed, and his teeth less likely to decay.

In addition to good food, every baby needs fresh air, sunshine, and from eighteen to twenty-two hours of sleep a day. Care for and feed the baby regularly. Then let him lie quietly the rest of the time. Do not toss him in the air or take him up every time he cries.

At the end of two months of well-planned meals, Alice and Tom Irving were so much improved in health, and were getting on so much better at school, that Mrs. Irving was thoroughly convinced of the importance of proper food. The more she thought about her family of six children, the more clearly she could see that their manner of living was not such as to insure the greatest amount of health and strength. She realized that if her children were to go out into the world to accomplish things requiring strength, a steady nerve, and endurance, she must do her part by fortifying them with, and teaching them to eat, the kind of food this marvelous machine, the human body, needs.

Although Mrs. Irving felt she had little time in which to learn and to put into practice a new order of eating, she was a sensible and a far-seeing woman and was determined to make the effort. She was all the more determined when one day Alice said: "Mother, if you had made me eat the things that were good for me before, perhaps I should not have lost that prize for scholarship." Alice made this remark laughingly, for what she really meant was, "If I had only made myself do it!" Mrs. Irving pondered: Would she be confronted by a more serious charge when the children were grown men and women? Would she be responsible for their lack of success if they failed because of insufficient strength and vitality?

"An ounce of prevention is worth a pound of cure," she said. "While it may take two or even five years to teach the children to like the things that are good for them, and to learn to eat them at the proper time and in the proper way, if I can save them from years of regret later, it will be time well spent."

BABY BETTY — ONE YEAR OLD

A well baby. Mrs. Irving had taken Betty to her family physician every three months for a physical examination, as does every wise mother, and she had followed his directions faithfully. As a result, Betty was the picture of health; she had good color, she was lively and good-natured, she digested her food well, she had regular bowel movements daily, and she gained in weight steadily. A well baby gains from four to seven ounces a week during the first six months of life and from two to four ounces a week during the last six months of the first year.

As weight was one way in which Mrs. Irving could tell whether or not Betty was developing normally, she weighed her regularly once a week; and in case of a loss in weight or a gain less than she expected, she took her to the doctor to have him look her over. Mrs. Irving knew that any little upset might soon become serious.

The best food. Baby Betty had been fortunate in that it had been possible for her mother to give her the food nature intended her to have — her mother's milk. Mother's milk has just the amount of protein, phosphorus, calcium, and iron that the growing baby needs to provide for the daily increase in the size of its bones and muscles, and enough fat and carbohydrate to furnish energy for kicking, crying, and playing for the first few months of life. But mother's milk must not be depended on for all the vitamins needed.

Foods other than milk. Experience has shown that children are stronger and healthier when they have additional vitamins supplied through foods other than mother's milk. Vitamin D is necessary from the beginning of life to put strength and durability into tissues, bones, and teeth while they are forming. When the supply of vitamin D is deficient, the chest bones become misshapen, the enamel of the teeth, formed before the teeth come through the gums, will be imperfect and decay early; the structure of bony tissues will be weaker; the legs may become bowed; and pneumonia and other diseases of the respiratory tract are likely to occur. These conditions are all manifestations of a deficiency of vitamin D and are the chief effects of a disease called rickets; a shortage of vitamin C may be the main cause of the defects in the teeth. Although the layman often thinks that bow-legs are the only result of rickets, the serious effects of the disease begin long before the legs show any sign of crookedness.

As mother's milk may be deficient in vitamin D, most physicians advise cod-liver oil, the richest known source of vitamin D, for all babies. The Children's Bureau of Washington, D. C., recommends the following amounts:

One half teaspoonful twice a day from two to six weeks of age.[1]

One teaspoonful twice a day from six weeks to three months of age.[1]

One teaspoonful three times a day from three months to two years of age.[1]

Egg yolk is another source of vitamin D which may be given in addition to the cod-liver oil (egg white should not be given during the first year, at least). Cod-liver oil and egg yolk are rich in both vitamin A and vitamin D, and both these vitamins are involved in developing a strong respiratory system and resistance to such diseases as pneumonia, tuberculosis, grippe, and common colds.

Some doctors advise egg yolk as early as the second month; it should be given by the sixth month at the latest. Egg yolk adds iron as well as vitamins A and D. Although the baby comes into the world with enough iron in its tissues to make iron-rich foods unnecessary for the first few months of life, it is advisable

[1] The giving of cod-liver oil may be discontinued during hot weather.

to add foods valuable for iron as early as the sixth month, and perhaps before.

With too little vitamin C a baby may lose his appetite, he may not make average gains in weight, and he may be irritable and restless, or he may have swollen and inflamed gums and joints; these conditions are mild symptoms of scurvy. Mother's milk usually contains enough C to prevent the development of scurvy, but oftentimes it does not contain enough to insure complete absence of all its symptoms. Some babies are more subject to scurvy than others, so it is well to provide a liberal amount of vitamin C as a health insurance. To avoid a deficiency of vitamin C, doctors advise giving to all babies orange or tomato juice. The usual quantity advised is one teaspoonful of juice, diluted with an equal amount of cool, boiled water during the first month; this amount is gradually increased from month to month, as indicated in the Schedule for Feeding Children during the First Year (Table XXIX).

With an insufficiency of vitamins B and G, babies fail to gain properly; frequently they have poor appetites; and their food is not always digested well. Since these vitamins are soluble in water, it is very simple to add them to the diet of the baby by giving him water in which vegetables have been boiled. The usual amount given is one to two teaspoonfuls of the vegetable water for a child four months old, with an increase to two tablespoonfuls plus some of the vegetable pulp, mashed and strained, by the sixth month. This water and pulp will supply iron and other mineral elements as well as vitamins B and G.

By the sixth or eighth month, extra energy must be supplied through cereals, well-cooked, strained, and diluted with milk or water. The kind of cereal is not important, but it is well to use those cereals from which the outer coating has not been removed, so as to add more mineral elements and vitamins.

The best substitute for mother's milk. Betty had a cousin who was less fortunate than she because it had not been possible for her to have mother's milk. She had, however, been fed the best substitute, cow's milk, with such additional foods as were given to Betty; and, with extreme care on the part of her mother, she was well and healthy too.

Cow's milk has the right amount of growing material for the calf, just as mother's milk has for the baby, but the calf grows more rapidly than the baby and needs a different proportion of energy and growing materials. When cow's milk is to be fed to babies, its composition must be changed or modified to make it more like mother's milk. This is called modified milk. It is difficult to know how to modify milk to make it just right for each individual child, as the changes made must vary with the age, weight, and strength of the child, and his ability to digest it. The larger child naturally requires more nourishment than the smaller one of the same age. A very active child requires more than a quiet one, and much crying increases the demand for energy considerably. Not all children can digest the same amount of food. Too much food may weaken the digestive system for life. The amount given should be adapted to the ability of the child to digest it. All these things must be considered, and it is very important to go to a doctor who will prescribe the best formula for each child.   Table XXVIII suggests a formula for the first year in case no specific directions are given, but it should be used only as a guide.   Table XXIX suggests the kind and amount of supplementary food (other than milk) which should be given to bottle-fed and to breast-fed babies during the first year.

The energy requirement of a child during the first year of his life may be stated briefly as follows:[1]

First three months, about 50 Calories per pound of body weight.

Second three months, about 45 Calories per pound of body weight.

Rest of the first year, about 40 Calories per pound of body weight.

PROBLEM

57. To determine the food requirement of a baby six months old, weighing 14 pounds:

Calculate energy supplied by the formula in Table XXVIII for a six months' old baby.   Is it adequate?   How much protein does it provide?   What percentage of the Calories is supplied by the protein?

Number of feedings a day.   The hours at which food is given are not important so long as it is given at the same time each day **by the clock,** with the same length of time between each two feedings during the day. Ordinarily, a baby has six or seven feedings every twenty-four hours during the first three months, then five or six feedings for the next six months, and four

[1] From Rose, *Feeding the Family*.

or five feedings for the rest of the first year; but the number of feedings and the amount of food will vary with the strength of the baby and the amount he is able to take at one time, and are best determined by the physician who knows the child and his particular needs.   One of the schedules on page 173 may be used if no directions as to time have been received, however.

TABLE XXVIII. — SUGGESTED FORMULÆ FOR MODIFIED MILK FOR A BOTTLE-FED BABY (Based on Holt and Shaw's *Save the Babies;* published by the American Medical Association)

TIME	MILK IN OUNCES	WATER IN OUNCES [4](BOILED AND COOLED)	SUGAR [1]	FEEDINGS [3]
1st and 2d days		1 to 3 tbsp. every 3 hrs.		
3d and 4th days	3	7	2 tsp.	7
5th, 6th, and 7th days	4	8	1 tbsp.	7
8th day	5	10	1½ tbsp.	7
8th day to end of 3d month	Increase ½ oz. every 4 days	Increase ½ oz. every 8 days	Increase ½ tbsp. every 2 wks.	7–6
End of 3d month	16	16	3 tbsp.	6
First of 4th month to end of 6th month	Increase ½ oz. every 6 days	Reduce by ½ oz. every 2 weeks. (Cook barley in the water if food is not well digested) [2]	3 tbsp.	6–5
End of 6th month	24	12	3 tbsp.	5
First of 7th month to end of 9th month	Increase ½ oz. every week if child is digesting food well and seems hungry	Reduce by ½ oz. every 2 wks.	3 tbsp.	5
End of 9th month	30	Cereal gruel (3 tbsp. of cereal cooked in 10 oz. water)	2 tbsp.	5
First of 10th month to end of 12th month	Increase 1 oz. per month	Cereal gruel (as above)	Reduce by 1 tbsp. per month	5–4

[1] Milk sugar is best, but malt sugar may be used.

[2] Barley water: cook ½ tbsp. barley flour in the water with which the milk is to be diluted, for twenty minutes. Cool before adding to the milk. Or, one or two ounces of limewater may be added to the milk if it is hard to digest.

[3] Time between feedings: 3 hrs. up to the 6th month, 4 hrs. after 6th month. Up to 4th month, 1 night feeding between 10 P.M. and 6 A.M. After 4th month, no night feeding after 10 P.M.

[4] Give an ounce of cool, boiled water two or three times a day between feedings.

Feeding Times for the Baby

1	2	3
6 A.M.	6:30 A.M.	7:00 A.M.
10 A.M.	10:30 A.M.	10:30 A.M.
2 P.M.	2:30 P.M.	2:00 P.M.
6 P.M.	6:00 P.M.	5:30 P.M.
10 P.M. [1]	10:00 P.M. [1]	10:00 P.M. [1]
2 A.M. [1]	2:00 A.M. [1]	2:00 A.M. [1]

[1] Discontinue the 2 A.M. feeding after the third month and the 10 P.M. feeding at the end of the ninth or tenth month if a child is growing normally.

Weaning the baby. Betty was weaned when she was seven months old to avoid a change of food in hot weather; otherwise she would not have been weaned until the eighth or ninth month. But because she was well she made normal gains throughout the weaning period. With such additional foods as are now given during the first year, weaning time may be earlier, is less trying, and is accompanied by less disturbance than formerly. The child is in a better physical condition to stand the change from mother's to cow's milk, and he or she should be accustomed to taking food from a cup. But as each child presents a different problem, it is best to have a doctor's advice with regard to the weaning time of each baby.

Cow's milk with none of the cream removed is the best substitute for mother's milk, but during the early days of weaning it must be diluted and otherwise modified according to the needs of the child. The formula for modifying milk will vary with the age and health of the individual. Weaning must be done very gradually. First, one bottle of modified milk is substituted for the afternoon breast feeding; if the baby has suffered no ill effects at the end of two

TABLE XXIX. — SUPPLEMENTARY FOODS DURING THE FIRST YEAR FOR BOTH BREAST-FED AND BOTTLE-FED BABIES

TIME / AGE IN MONTHS	COD-LIVER OIL	ORANGE OR TOMATO JUICE	EGG YOLK (NO WHITE)	VEGETABLE		CEREAL [2]	BREAD
				WATER	PULP		
1st month	½ tsp. twice a day	1 tsp. diluted with 1 tsp. cool, boiled water					
2nd month	1 tsp. twice a day (at 6 wks.)	1 tsp. diluted with 1 tsp. cool, boiled water	(Egg yolk may be given *Cautiously*)				
3rd month	1 tsp. twice a day	2 tsp. diluted with 2 tsp. cool, boiled water	Egg yolk may be given				
4th month	1 tsp. twice a day	2 tsp. diluted with 2 tsp. cool, boiled water	Egg yolk may be given	1 tsp. strained [1]			
5th month	1 tsp. twice a day	2 tsp. diluted with 2 tsp. cool, boiled water	Egg yolk may be given	2 tsp. strained			
6th month	1 tsp. three times a day	1 tbsp. diluted with 1 tbsp. cool, boiled water	½ egg yolk every other day	1 to 2 tbsp. strained	½ tsp. strained	½ tsp. every 3 or 4 days, increasing to 1 tbsp. daily at end of month	
7th month	1 tsp. three times a day	1 tbsp. diluted with 1 tbsp. cool, boiled water	½ egg yolk every other day	1 to 2 tbsp. strained	1 tsp. strained (first 2 wks.) 2 tsp. strained (3rd and 4th wk.)	1 to 1½ tbsp. twice a day (2 to 3 tbsp. a day)	

TABLE XXIX (Continued)

Time Age in Months	Cod-liver Oil	Orange or Tomato Juice	Egg Yolk (No White)	Vegetable			Cereal [2]	Bread
				Water	Pulp			
8th month	1 tsp. three times a day	1 tbsp. diluted with 1 tbsp. cool boiled water	½ egg yolk every other day	1 to 2 tbsp. strained	1 tbsp. strained		4 tbsp. a day (2 tbsp. both morning and evening meals)	
9th month	1 tsp. three times a day	2 tbsp. diluted with 2 tbsp. cool, boiled water	½ egg yolk every other day	Gradually decrease	1½ tbsp. strained		4 tbsp. a day (2 tbsp. both morning and evening meals)	1 piece dry toast or zwieback
10th month	1 tsp. three times a day	Make less dilute	½ egg yolk every other day	Discontinue	2 tbsp. strained		4 tbsp. a day (2 tbsp. both morning and evening meals)	1 piece dry toast or zwieback
11th month	1 tsp. three times a day	2 to 3 tbsp. undiluted orange or tomato juice	½ egg yolk every other day		2 to 3 tbsp. strained vegetable pulp		4 tbsp. a day (2 tbsp. both morning and evening meals)	1 piece dry toast or zwieback
12th month	1 tsp. three times a day	2 to 3 tbsp. undiluted orange or tomato juice	½ egg yolk every other day		2 to 3 tbsp. strained vegetable pulp		Make cereal gruel less dilute	1 piece dry toast or zwieback

[1] Some doctors give vegetable water earlier to bottle-fed babies.

[2] Cream of wheat, farina, or oatmeal (strained); make like cereal and dilute with an equal amount of milk.

weeks, another bottle of modified milk is given in
place of the 10 A.M. breast feeding; after another
week or two, the third bottle is substituted for the
6 P.M. breast feeding; finally the fourth bottle is given
at 6 A.M.

Regularity of meals is essential. Every book consulted by Mrs. Irving, and every mother she knew who
had a happy, contented baby of her own, said that regularity in both eating and sleeping was the first essential
for the health and future disposition of the child.
Some doctors say that many cases of dissatisfaction
and irritability in older boys and girls may be traced
to poor food habits established during the first two or
three years of life. Betty had been fed quite regularly
until within the last few months, when she discovered
that she could get something to eat whenever she
cried long and loud enough; and like the rest of the
children she was beginning to have only the things she
liked best. Mrs. Irving decided to train Betty differ-
ently. She made a schedule of her food and pinned it
on the wall beside the clock. The schedule was as
follows:

Feeding Schedule for Betty — One Year of Age

Breakfast: 7:00 A.M.

Cereal	¼ to ⅓ cupful thoroughly cooked and strained rolled oats, oatmeal, wheatena, or other dark cereal
Bread	1 small piece, oven-dried or toasted, or 1 piece of zwieback
Milk	1 cupful (warmed in cold weather)

At 9:00 A.M.

Fruit	1 to 3 tablespoonfuls baked apple, prune pulp, orange juice, or baked banana.

Luncheon: 10:30 A.M.

Milk	1 cupful (warmed in cold weather)
Bread	as at breakfast

Dinner: 2:00 P.M.

Soup	½ cupful milk and 1 tablespoonful cereal
Egg yolk or liver	1 tablespoonful liver or ½ egg yolk
Vegetable	1 to 2 tablespoonfuls boiled and mashed spinach, carrots, green peas, string beans, celery, lettuce, squash, mild turnip, or chard
Bread	1 piece oven-dried or toasted, or 1 piece of zwieback (may be omitted)
Milk	½ cupful (warmed in cold weather)

Supper: 5:30 P.M.

Cereal	as at breakfast
Milk	1 cupful, warmed in cold weather

The Calorie and protein content of Betty's food at one year of age is shown in Table XXX.

Mrs. Irving felt sure Betty would cry for fifteen or twenty minutes at first, but she had been told that she must not depart from the schedule if she wanted the experiment to be successful. Betty did cry for fifteen minutes the first time her desire for something to eat was not gratified, and then she fell asleep, exhausted. When gently aroused at the scheduled hour, she took her food with more eagerness than she had shown for some time. She not only cried frequently during the first day without results, but she felt very much abused all the rest of that week. Occasionally some member of the family who also felt she was being abused would feed her, but this only gave her courage to cry more vigorously next time.

Mrs. Irving had to enlist the coöperation of the whole family before she finally had Betty trained to

TABLE XXX. — CALORIE AND PROTEIN VALUE OF THE DIET OF A CHILD ONE YEAR OF AGE: 840 TO 920 CALORIES

FOOD	QUANTITY		CALORIES	PROTEIN
	AMOUNT	WEIGHT IN		
		Ounces		Grams
Breakfast:				
Cereal	⅓ cupful	3.2 (0.3 oz., dry)	40	1.7
Bread	1 slice	0.7	50	1.8
Milk	1 cupful	8.0	160	8.0
9:00 A.M.				
Fruit (orange juice)	2 tbsp.	1.0	6	. . . .
Luncheon:				
Milk	1 cupful	8.0	160	8.0
Bread	1 slice	0.7	50	1.8
Dinner:				
Egg yolk . . .	½ egg yolk	0.3	28	1.4
Milk	1 cupful	8.0	160	8.0
Cereal	1 tbsp.	0.6	12	0.5
Vegetable (carrot) .	2 tbsp.	0.5	5	. . . .
Supper:				
Milk	1 cupful	8.0	160	8.0
Cereal	⅓ cupful	3.2 (0.3 oz., dry)	40	1.7
Totals	. . . .	. . . .	870	40.9

know that food would be given to her only at stated hours. If any one through mistaken kindness smuggled a cracker or a piece of cake or candy to her, there was always sure to follow a "tempest," until finally everyone learned that absolute regularity was the only safe rule.

By the end of a month Betty was reconciled to her new mode of living and accepted water as a substitute for food between meals as a matter of course.

Every child should have cool, boiled water to drink from two to three times a day, given midway between feedings, but never just before or just after a feeding, unless ordered by a physician.

Add new foods gradually. Tom was usually the guilty one in tempting Betty, but when he finally realized that he must not give her a bite of whatever he might be eating, he said: "That's reasonable. It is just like the boys who are training in athletics. We do easy things at first and are able to do harder and harder work gradually. A boy may injure himself for life by trying to do things too hard for him at first, but which would be easy for him after several years of practice."

Tom was right. A baby must be given new foods cautiously so as to train his digestive tract to take them without injury. If a child does not like a new food the first time it is offered to him, it may be the strangeness of it that he refuses; he may learn to like it upon further acquaintance. One way in which to teach a child to like a new food is to let him taste it daily, or every other day, until it becomes familiar to him, gradually increasing the amount until he will take a teaspoonful, then a tablespoonful. This may take a week, or it may take a month, or even longer. It will be very hard to teach a child to like a new food if, when he refuses to take it, something more appetizing is given in place of it.

Select clean milk. Too much care cannot be used in selecting the best milk for the baby. By referring to Charts I and II in Chapter I we see that a child gains more pounds during the first twelve months of its life, while milk is its main source of nourishment, than during any other period of the same length of time. Because milk normally forms such a large part of the diet of the child during this rapidly growing period, if anything is wrong with the milk at this time, it will influence the health of the child much more quickly than later, when other foods are equally prominent in the diet.

Keep the milk clean. Milk is a very fertile garden for germs. They grow rapidly in it unless the milk is kept cold. If the baby drinks milk in which germs have been growing, there is grave danger of illness. Every precaution, then, should be taken

1. To get clean milk
2. To keep it clean by putting it only into clean utensils
3. To keep it cold
4. To keep it covered, so as to prevent germs in the air from falling into it
5. To wash off the top of the bottle before opening, so that any germs on the mouth of the bottle will not enter the first cupful poured out
6. To pour no milk back into the bottle after it has once been poured out, as it may collect germs on the way (If no more than is needed is poured out, there will be no temptation to return any to the bottle.)
7. Boil for three minutes any milk which is to be given to the baby. This destroys the germs and makes the milk slightly laxative.

PROBLEM

58. To keep milk cold without a refrigerator:

(a) Materials needed:

A wooden box about 18 inches square

A tin pail deep enough to hold a milk bottle

Sawdust, excelsior, or pieces of paper (crumpled) for packing

Cover the bottom of the box with a layer of packing to a depth of four inches, set the pail in the middle of the box, and fill the space between the pail and the sides of the box with sawdust, excelsior, or crumpled paper (if paper or excelsior is used it must be packed in very solid). Set the milk bottle in the pail and surround with ice, broken in small pieces. Cover with many thicknesses of newspaper and set in a shady place.

(b) Set the milk bottles in cold water and change the water frequently. The water must come to the neck of the bottle.

(c) Wrap a wet cloth around the milk bottle, with one end of the cloth dipped in a pan of cold water and set in a shady place where the wind blows over it.

Try each of these methods, and determine the temperature of the milk at the end of three hours in each case.

The care of the feeding bottles is very important. The best milk may be spoiled and the healthiest baby made ill by improper care of the feeding bottles and nipples. The following suggestions should insure the baby against danger from this source:

Feeding bottles:

Rinse the bottle in cold water as soon as the baby has finished his meal (do not let the milk sour in it).

Wash with hot water and soapsuds; then scald in boiling water.

Boil for ten or fifteen minutes once a day.

Stopper with clean cotton, and keep stoppered until used.

Nipples:

Wash inside and out, first with cold water and then with hot water.   Boil.

Keep in a dry, sterile jar when not in use.

After boiling the nipple, let nothing touch that part which the baby puts in his mouth.

To test the flow or the temperature of milk, shake some of it out on the back of the hand, but do not under any circumstances put the nipple to the lips.

Other health habits. The very best food that can be given will not make well-nourished children unless it is accompanied by other good health habits.   In addition to the right food, babies need plenty of sleep, fresh air, and sunshine.

Babies under six months of age need from 18 to 22 hours of sleep out of each 24 hours.

Babies from six months to one year of age need from 17 to 19 hours of sleep out of each 24 hours.

They should be in the fresh air for at least two hours a day, and longer if possible. Many mothers who are unable to take the baby out of doors, throw all the windows open in one room, even in winter, and put the baby in his carriage near one of the windows, where he can breathe fresh air without being in a draft.

In accordance with what was learned in Chapter VI (namely, that the rays of the sun on the bare skin help babies to grow straight and strong), doctors suggest that each baby have his arms and legs exposed to the sun for a short time each pleasant day. **Caution** is necessary, because harm may result from overex-

B   A
Courtesy of Professor E. B. Hart, Wisconsin Agricultural Experiment Station

Illustration No. 8. — The influence of sunlight on the growth of two chickens; Chicken A was in the sunlight for one half hour each day, while Chicken B had no sunlight

posure. All babies do not react in the same way to this treatment: dark-complexioned children can stand more sun without burning than those with light complexion; and red-haired children burn **very** easily. It is best to begin with an exposure of only the arms for five minutes a day and gradually increase to one half hour; then, in the same way, gradually accustom the legs to the sun, until they may be exposed for one half hour without burning. For safety, each mother should obtain directions from some one who understands how to give the treatment without burning. Illustration No. 8 shows the difference in the rate of growth between two chickens, one of which was in the sun for one half hour each day and the other of which was deprived of the benefits of the sun's rays.

PROBLEMS

59. Prepare a day's meals for Betty and her cousin, following the schedule given on page 176.

60. Calculate the food value of the meals prepared in terms of energy and protein. How much energy is needed by a child one year old, weighing 20 pounds? Is the food value of Betty's diet sufficient for a child her age?

61. Estimate the cost of feeding a child one year old, for one day and for one week.

QUESTIONS

1. How did Mrs. Irving keep track of Betty's physical condition?

2. Why is mother's milk the best food for the baby during the first year?

3. In what factor may mother's milk be deficient? How has this deficiency been supplied in recent years? Explain what may happen if this deficiency is not supplied.

4. How does a lack of vitamin C affect the baby? Explain how vitamin C may be added to the diet of the baby.

5. How may vitamins B and G be added to the diet of the baby?

6. Explain why cow's milk must be modified to meet the needs of a baby. Who should prescribe the formula?

7. Why is the regularity with which a baby is fed, so important? Suggest a schedule for the feeding of the baby during the first year.

8. New foods should be added to the diet of a baby very gradually. How do you think young children can be taught to eat foods they need but do not like?

9. Completion test:

All babies should have —— —— —— to supply vitamin D.

A baby twelve months old and weighing 22 pounds needs —— Calories daily.

A baby should have orange or tomato juice added to his diet at the end of the —— month.

Besides milk, a baby needs to drink —— several times a day.

REFERENCES

For students:

ROSE, MARY S. *Feeding the Family*, third edition, Chapter V. The Macmillan Company (1929).

WEST, MRS. MAX. *Infant Care.* (Pamphlet.) Children's Bureau, U. S. Department of Labor, Washington, D. C.

——. *Child Care.* (Pamphlet.) Children's Bureau, U. S. Department of Labor, Washington, D. C.

For teachers:

The Baby in the House of Health. (Pamphlet.) The American Child Health Association, 370 Seventh Avenue, New York City.

MOORE, C. U. *Nutrition of Mother and Child.* J. P. Lippincott (1923).

ROBERTS, L. J. *Nutrition Work with Children.* The University of Chicago Press (1926).

ROSE, MARY S. *Foundations of Nutrition*, Chapter XII, pages 395 to 399; 445 to 463. The Macmillan Company (1927).

CHAPTER X

FOOD DURING THE SECOND YEAR

WHEN children begin to walk about, they are all too apt to be given the privileges of grown-ups. But if they are to enjoy those same privileges when they are old enough to appreciate them, the same careful attention as has been described for the first year must continue throughout the growing period. During the second year a child still needs very easily digested food, simply prepared and given at regular hours. He should have cod-liver oil, sunshine, and long hours of sleep.

Importance of food during the second year. With Betty once more on a regular schedule, Mrs. Irving breathed a sigh of relief — a thankful sigh — as she thought of the danger into which Betty's finicky appetite had been leading her. And she was truly grateful when told that she had little to fear for Betty's safety during the second summer, now that she was having plenty of milk, vegetables, fruit, and whole grain cereals, with the cod-liver oil, her sun baths, long hours of sleep, and regular hours for eating and sleeping. But there were many other things to think about, so Mrs. Irving made a list of them to insure attention to each point. Alice, who was interested in a nursery school near by, helped her mother formulate the following:

Schedule for Betty's Second Year

1. Weigh Betty once a month. Average weight during the second year is from 20 to 28 pounds. A continued loss in weight or a failure to gain means that something is wrong, and little things may soon become serious. (However, mothers should not worry over slight variations in weight.)

2. Arrange regular hours for rest and sleep. Betty should have from 12 to 14 hours of sleep at night, with morning and afternoon naps of 1 to 2 hours each.

3. Put Betty out of doors when she takes her nap if possible; otherwise, by an open window. Windows should be open at night.

4. Arrange to have her out in the sunshine at least one half hour each pleasant day, with legs and arms bared when weather is warm enough to permit.

5. Brush her teeth twice a day, using a small brush with uneven, medium-stiff bristles.

6. Each day, give her something hard to chew to increase circulation in the jaws and thus help to strengthen the teeth. Give crisp toast, zwieback, or hard crackers.

7. Continue cod-liver oil; one teaspoonful three times a day during cool weather.

8. Serve four nourishing meals a day until the fourteenth month; then gradually decrease

the extra meal, so that when two years old she will be getting three meals a day.

9. Allow no one to give Betty any food between meals. *This is very important.*

10. Give her plenty of water to drink between meals.

11. Make sure that there is at least one regular bowel movement daily. Plenty of water to drink, vegetables, fresh fruit, coarse cereals, and exercise will stimulate proper elimination; if this does not follow, then consult a doctor.

12. Take Betty to the doctor for a complete physical examination twice a year and thus help to prevent sickness.

MEALS DURING THE SECOND YEAR

Mrs. Irving was anxious to give Betty every possible chance of becoming a strong, vigorous, and fine-looking girl, so she planned her meals with a great deal of care. She knew that the child's food must be very simple but nourishing and easily digested.

Milk for growth. The basis of Betty's diet was a quart of milk for its excellent (complete) growth proteins, its calcium, so essential for bones and teeth during these early years, and its vitamin A, as well as its other food factors. There was added an egg yolk or a tablespoonful of liver every day for additional protein, for iron and other mineral elements, and for vitamins. Egg yolk provides vitamin D, which is necessary for straight bones and sound teeth, but, for safety, Mrs. Irving decided to give Betty cod-liver oil as an extra precaution against rickets and poor teeth.

(She gave the child sun baths in addition, as she wanted Betty to have every opportunity for a high resistance to disease in later years.)

The indispensable vegetable. The diet, as planned, included plenty of vegetables for mineral elements and vitamins, without which good growth and good health are impossible. Vegetables also stimulate and regulate all the internal activities, including bowel movements. This daily elimination is **very important.** Betty was scheduled to have from two to three tablespoonfuls of a dark green, leafy vegetable, especially valuable for iron and vitamin A (see Group I below), alternating with the same quantity of one of the vegetables given in Group II. Dry beans and peas in soups were added for energy, protein, mineral elements, and vitamins B and G. Mrs. Irving made a note on the diet list to the effect that she must add a tablespoonful of baked potato by the fourteenth or fifteenth month; the potato adds more protein, iron and other mineral elements, and vitamins. All vegetables should be carefully mashed or strained throughout the second year.

SELECT ONE VEGETABLE FROM EACH GROUP ON ALTERNATE DAYS

Group I		Group II	
Asparagus	Green peas	Carrots	Squash
Beet tops	Spinach	Cauliflower	Tomato
Chard	String beans	Celery	Turnip, mild
Dandelions	Turnip tops	Onions, young	Dry beans and peas in soups
Lettuce	Any other green leaf		

PROBLEM

62. To review the cooking of vegetables:

Of the vegetables listed in Groups I and II, cook those in season. Use very little water, so as to retain all the mineral elements and vitamins possible. Season lightly, put the vegetables through a sieve, and arrange servings suitable for a child of Betty's age.

Fruit is essential. In the books Mrs. Irving had been reading, she had learned the value of citrus fruits, such as oranges, tangerines, and grapefruit, so she added from two to three tablespoonfuls of juice from one of these fruits daily; she noted on her schedule that tomato may be given in place of the citrus fruit, as it also contains vitamin C, the factor which makes citrus fruit so important a part of the diet. In addition to this fresh fruit, she planned to give Betty the pulp of two prunes a day to add more iron. Toward the end of the second year, there may be given occasionally two or three tablespoonfuls of baked banana, stewed dates, stewed or baked pear or apple, and cooked fresh or dried peaches or apricots, in place of the prunes.

PROBLEM

63. To prepare fruit juice and to review the cooking of fruits:

Prepare orange or grapefruit juice; strain out the large pieces of pulp.

Stew prunes slowly without sugar.

Bake bananas slowly in the skins, adding no sugar. Put the pulp through a sieve.

Arrange amounts of these fruits suitable for a child the age of Betty.

Cereals and bread for energy and for vitamins B and G. After the first year a child may eat any cereal, the chief consideration being thorough cooking and an amount sufficient to provide Calories for normal gains. A child will not gain properly if Calories are low. Mrs. Irving studied the various cereals available, but finally decided to give both Betty and the rest of the family only those cereals from which the outer coating of the grain has not been removed; she had read that these cereals furnish extra iron and other mineral elements and vitamins, especially vitamin B. As there is danger of a deficiency of the latter food factor unless whole grains are used, every child should have some whole grain product at least once a day. Oatmeal and other coarse cereals contain particles of husk that are likely to irritate the intestinal tract of very young children. Therefore such cereals should be strained before feeding to children under fifteen or sixteen months of age.

Meat. Mrs. Irving and Alice were cautious about giving muscle meat to Betty, because it is too stimulating for a growing child and is thought to cause convulsions in some children. And with a quart of milk, an egg yolk, or a tablespoonful of liver every day, and plenty of green vegetables, meat is unnecessary. Broth may be used as a carrier of rice or barley and vegetables two or three times a week, however.

Butter and sugar. Another notation made on the schedule was a reminder that butter should not be given to children until the fourteenth or fifteenth month, when one half teaspoonful may be used in some way during the day, either on toast or on potato.

Sugar — well, it so often becomes the master instead of a valuable servant that Mrs. Irving decided to postpone the giving of sugar to Betty until well into the last half of the second year, when she thought it might be safe to add from one to two teaspoonfuls per day in cooked fruit and simple desserts, such as custards, junket, and cornstarch or rice pudding.

The food value of the diets. After the meals were planned, Alice calculated the food value, to make sure Calories, protein, calcium, phosphorus, and iron were adequate. With the 32 grams of protein, 1 + gram of calcium, and almost 1 gram of phosphorus in a quart of milk, together with additional amounts from grain products, these foodstuffs seemed to be abundantly provided. Alice was sure the vitamins were richly supplied through milk, egg yolk, fruit, vegetables, liver, and cod-liver oil, but she was not so sure about the iron. She and her mother intended to provide a generous amount of iron, because they wanted to make it possible for Betty to have the charm and vivacity that can come only with good red blood. And a little figuring convinced them that the iron content of the diet would be ample if Betty had, in addition to her quart of milk, an egg yolk or one tablespoonful of liver, a generous serving of some green leafy vegetable, a whole grain cereal each day, and the two prunes which Mrs. Irving had planned to give. But the absence of any one of the above-mentioned foods would make the iron lower than the allowance of 0.005 gram, which was the goal they wanted to reach. It seemed best to let Betty have white bread once a day at least, as they were afraid she would

TABLE XXXI. — MEALS FOR A CHILD FROM FOURTEEN TO EIGHTEEN MONTHS OF AGE (920 to 1050 Calories)

FOOD	QUANTITY		CALORIES	PROTEIN
	AMOUNT	WEIGHT		
		Ounces		*Grams*
Breakfast:				
7:00 to 7:30 A.M.				
Cereal [1]	⅓ cup	3.0 (0.4 oz., dry)	40	1.5
Milk	1 cup	8.0	160	8.0
Bread	1 slice	0.7	50	1.8
Butter	½ tsp.	0.08	16	..
Fruit Juice:				
9:00 A.M.				
Orange juice . .	3 tbsp.	1.5	18	..
Luncheon:				
10:00 to 11:00 A.M.				
Bread	1 slice	0.7	50	1.8
Milk	1 cup	8.0	160	8.0
Dinner:				
1:30 to 2:30 P.M.				
Egg yolk, liver, bean soup, or broth with rice .			50 (average)	2.8
Potato, baked . .	1 tbsp.	0.6	14	..
Vegetable . . .	2 tbsp.	1.9	10 (average)	..
Milk	1 cup	8.0	160	8.0
Bread	½ slice	0.35	25	0.9
Supper:				
5:00 to 6:00 P.M.				
Cereal [1]	⅓ cup	3.0 (0.4 oz., dry)	40	1.5
Milk	1 cup	8.0	160	8.0
Prune pulp . . .	2 tbsp.	1.0	40	..
Totals	. . . .	. . . .	993	42.3

[1] Oatmeal, wheatena, pettijohn's, ralston, malt breakfast food, and similar cereals from which the outer coating has not been removed

TABLE XXXII. — MEALS FOR A CHILD FROM EIGHTEEN TO TWENTY-FOUR MONTHS OF AGE   (1050 to 1200 Calories)

FOOD	QUANTITY		CALORIES	PROTEIN
	AMOUNT	WEIGHT		
		Ounces		*Grams*
Breakfast:				
7:00 to 7:30 A.M.				
Cereal [1] . . .	½ cup	4.8 (0.5 oz., dry)	60	2.5
Milk	1 cup	8.0	160	8.0
Bread	1 slice	0.7	50	1.8
Butter	1 tsp.	0.15	33	..
Fruit	3 tbsp.	1.5 (average)	18 (average)	..
Dinner:				
11:30 A.M. to 12 M.				
Egg, liver, bean soup, or broth with cereal and vegetables . .			75 (average)	4.2
Potato, baked . .	1 med.	3.0	100	2.8
Another vegetable	2 to 3 tbsp.	2.5 (average)	15 (average)	..
Milk	1 cup	8.0	160	8.0
Bread	1 slice	0.7	50	1.8
Plain dessert (not very sweet) . .	¼ cup	2.7	40	2.0
Supper:				
5:00 to 5:30 P.M.				
Cereal [1] . . .	½ cup	4.8 (0.5 oz., dry)	60	2.5
Bread	1 slice	0.7	50	1.8
Milk	1 cup	8.0	160	8.0
Prune pulp . .	2 tbsp.	1.0	40	..
Totals	. . . .	. . . .	1071	43.4

[1] Oatmeal, wheatena, pettijohn's, ralston, malt breakfast or other similar whole grain cereal

not eat enough dark bread to satisfy her Calorie requirement.

How many meals a day? The food as planned was then distributed according to meals, four meals for the first half of the second year and three meals for the last half of the second year. At eighteen months of age, the mid-afternoon lunches are no longer necessary, and the fruit, given at 9 or 10 o'clock during the first half of the second year, may be given with the breakfast. The plan for the meals during the second year is given in Tables XXXI and XXXII. Meals for a child from twelve to fourteen months of age are given in Table XXX in Chapter IX.

Amount of food. The amount of food given throughout the second year will depend on the strength and size of the child. The chief variation will be made in bread and cereals, which should be adjusted to the individual child to maintain normal gains.

PROBLEM

64. Prepare a day's meals for a child of fourteen months, using Table XXXI.

Prepare a day's meals for a child of twenty-four months, using Table XXXII.

QUESTIONS

1. Why is the care of the child during the second year important?

2. Discuss the schedule planned for Betty by Alice and her mother.

3. What food continued to form the basis of Betty's diet? What foods were added for additional protein? What foods were added for vitamin D?

4. What was done to help to strengthen Betty's teeth?

5. List the vegetables that children may have during the second year.

6. What foods were added to supply vitamin C for Betty?

7. Why are cereals so important in the diet of a child?

8. Betty needed a generous supply of iron. Name the foods in her diet that are especially rich in iron.

9. Completion test:

> During the second year, children should eat —— between meals.
>
> Coarse cereals should be —— before they are given to children to eat.
>
> Do not give butter to children before the —— month.
>
> It is better not to add sugar to the diet of a child until the latter part of the —— year.

REFERENCES

For students:

HARRIS, J. W. and LACEY, E. V. *Everyday Foods*, pages 14 to 17; 366 and 367; 387 to 391. Houghton Mifflin Company (1927).

ROSE, MARY S. *Feeding the Family*, third edition, Chapter VI. The Macmillan Company (1929).

For teachers:

LUCAS, WILLIAM P., M.D. *The Health of the Runabout Child*. The Macmillan Company (1923).

ROBERTS, LYDIA. *Nutrition Work With Children*, The University of Chicago Press (1927).

CHAPTER XI

FOOD FOR CHILDREN FROM TWO TO FIVE YEARS OF AGE

AFTER the first two years of life, many children are all too often allowed to make unguided decisions with regard to food and other health habits. As a result, many of them suffer in later years because of irregular and unwise eating and irregular and insufficient sleep.

Careful attention to diet, sleep, rest, and exercise, and the giving of cod-liver oil throughout the growing period will mean much to the future health of boys and girls. Milk, vegetables, fruit, cod-liver oil, sunshine, and long hours of sleep are still fundamental for good growth, good teeth, and good health.

JACK'S DIET

Appearance is not always an indication of health. Jack appeared to be the picture of health. He weighed 34 pounds, which is average for his age of three years, and he had every indication of being well-fed, but Mrs. Irving had observed that many boys who are plump at three years seem to lose weight as they grow older. Dick, Jack's older brother, had seemed thin and pale of late, and now his mother thought she had at least one explanation for it. Perhaps his failure to gain normally was due to the fact that he had been allowed to fall into careless habits of eating, sleeping, and the like. At any rate, she decided to encourage her children to form good eating habits in the future.

She had read that Mendel, a prominent scientist of Yale University, had some rats that were fed a diet adequate in all respects except that the calcium was low. The rats thrived at first but suddenly became ill. After this same thing had happened with many rats, he concluded that perhaps many hitherto unexplained illnesses of boys and girls and men and women may be due to an insufficient amount of some one food factor, especially the calcium in milk.

Jack's diet. To protect Jack from the fate of the rats, Mrs. Irving made a very careful schedule for him, a schedule very much like the one she had made for Betty, except that Betty was to have longer hours of sleep, and Jack was allowed a little more varied diet, with quantities of food somewhat increased. The meals of a boy or girl from two to six years of age should consist only of those foods a young child can digest easily without interfering with, or overtaxing, the digestive system. Mrs. Irving interpreted this to mean that Jack's diet should consist chiefly of milk, vegetables, cereals, fruit, and eggs. The following is an outline of Jack's food needs:

One quart of milk daily

Potato every day, with a generous serving of one or two other vegetables from the lists below

Some citrus fruit; citrus fruit or tomato at least four or five times a week, with either the addition or the substitution of fresh or dried fruit on other days

An egg every other day, with fish, cottage cheese, or dry beans or peas in soups on other days

Plenty of bread and cereals to maintain normal gains in weight;
  dark cereals every day

One to three tablespoonfuls of sugar and one tablespoonful of
  butter or some other fat

One teaspoonful of cod-liver oil three times a day

Three meals a day. Mrs. Irving planned to give
the food listed above in three substantial and nourishing, but very simple, meals a day, as shown in Table
XXXIII. Thereafter Jack was to have nothing to eat
between meals. His food was planned also to overcome the condition of constipation which seemed of
late to be giving him headaches and an irritable disposition. At the end of this chapter are plans for the
meals of children four and five years of age; there is
also in Chapter XII a statement of the facts which
served as a warning to Mrs. Irving as well as a guide
in making the meals such as to overcome or prevent
constipation, not only for Jack but for the rest of the
family as well.

Milk, the Food That Has no Substitute

Milk is still the basis of the diet. Jack frequently
refused to drink milk. He sometimes had one and
occasionally two cups of milk a day, but more often
he had none at all. Milk is the only food that contains
enough calcium for bones, teeth, and other uses and
should be the chief growing material in the diet of all
boys and girls, even after they begin to take other
food. All children ought to have a quart of milk a
day until they are five or six years of age. Two to
three cups a day is the very smallest amount any
child under five years should have.

TABLE XXXIII. — MEALS FOR A CHILD DURING THE THIRD YEAR
1000 TO 1300 CALORIES   (37 to 43 Calories per pound)

| FOOD | QUANTITY | | CALORIES | PROTEIN |
	AMOUNT	WEIGHT		
		Ounces		*Grams*
Breakfast:				
7:00–7:30 A.M.				
Cereal	½ cupful	4.8	60	2.5
Milk for cereal and		(0.5 oz., dry)		
for drinking	1½ cupfuls	12.0	240	12.0
Bread	1 slice	0.7	50	1.8
Butter	1 tsp.	0.15	33	..
Fruit	3 tbsp.	1.5	18	..
		(average)	(average)	
Dinner:				
11:30 A.M.–12:00 M.				
Egg, fish, cottage				
cheese, or bean				
or pea soup . .			75	4.2
			(average)	(average)
Potato	1 medium	4.0	100	2.8
Other vegetables .	4 tbsp.	3.5	25	..
		(average)		
Milk	1 cupful	8.0	160	8.0
Bread	1 slice	0.7	50	1.8
Butter	1 tsp.	0.15	33	..
Plain dessert [1] .	⅓ cupful	3.6	50	2.5
		(average)	(average)	(average)
Supper:				
5:30–6:00 P.M.				
Cereal	½ cupful	4.8	60	2.5
		(0.5 oz., dry)		
Milk for cereal and				
for drinking	1 cupful	8.0	160	8.0
Bread	1 slice	0.7	50	1.8
Butter	1 tsp.	0.15	33	..
Prune pulp [2] . .	2 tbsp.	1.0	40	..
Totals		. . . .	1237	47.9

[1] For dessert serve custards, junket, cornstarch pudding, rice pudding, gelatin dessert, prune whip, or tapioca.
[2] Prune pulp may be varied with other cooked fruit near the end of the third year.

Jack's mother decided that he must have everything essential to promote growth, so she planned a quart of milk daily for him. The first day this rule went into effect Jack happened not to want the milk, but without arguing the question and thereby putting Jack into a bad humor, his mother read to him the story of the Three Bears. Then they played a game in which Jack was the Tiny Bear and his warm milk was the Bear's Soup. After this game his mother had little difficulty in persuading him to drink milk, provided it was warmed, put in a bowl, and called Bear's Soup.

Stories, games, and imagination will oftentimes accomplish what talking cannot do. It is better, however, to try the game before the feelings have been aroused to the point of obstinacy, as it is important that the child eat his food in a happy frame of mind so as to avoid interference with digestion. Stormy scenes caused by forced feeding are often more harmful than beneficial.

Oftentimes Jack's mother disguised a part of the milk in some cooked food, a change that helped considerably in incorporating the food value of a whole quart of milk a day into his diet. If after every known way has been tried, it is found that a child really cannot drink milk, the whole quart may be given in some cooked form, such as milk soups, milk toast, custards, junket, cocoa, or milk cooked in the cereal.

Too many people fail to recognize the part milk is going to play in the lives of the children in future years; in consequence they feel that milk is an extravagance and that tea and coffee are cheap substitutes.

This is a mistake, as no other food can supply the protein in so suitable a form and no other food can so well supply the amount of calcium and the vitamins needed by the body. Children will have a very poor chance of growing normally if they have no milk.

Tea and Coffee

Tea and coffee are not substitutes for milk. Milk is a real food, while tea and coffee are only stimulants

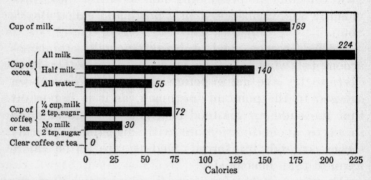

Chart XXIII. — Relative fuel value of milk, cocoa, and tea or coffee

without food value. Chart XXIII shows the relative value of a cup of milk, a cup of cocoa, and a cup of coffee or tea. All the food value in the cup of coffee or tea is supplied by the milk or sugar added. It would, therefore, be far better to take the milk without the stimulant and thus avoid injurious effects. Tea and coffee ought never to be given to children, even in milk. It is much better to drink half a cup of milk alone than half a cup of milk combined with half a cup of tea or coffee.

PROBLEM

65. Plan and compare two breakfasts, each consisting of 500 Calories:
    (*a*) Bread, jam, and coffee
    (*b*) Oatmeal and milk
    Calculate the protein and mineral content, and the cost of each
    breakfast.

CEREALS, BREADS, AND OTHER GRAIN PRODUCTS

As a child grows older, his weight will increase, he
will get more and more vigorous, and he will need more
energy and more growing materials than the quart
of milk will supply. The extra energy may best be
supplied at each meal by bread or cereal as a supplement to the milk. The bread or cereal will also increase the growing material. Every 100-Calorie portion of most grain products will increase the protein
by three or four grams. The mineral elements (especially iron) and the vitamins will vary with the type
of bread eaten. Oatmeal, rolled oats, barley, wheatena,
pettijohn's, ralston, malt breakfast food, brown rice,
and other similar dark cereals from which the outer
coating has not been removed in the manufacturing
process, contain more food value per pound than those
which have been highly refined.

PROBLEM

66. To become familiar with the grain products furnishing mineral
    elements in largest amounts (Consult tables in Chapters V
    and VI):
        List under "Calcium" the grain products giving more
    than 0.01 gram of calcium per 100 Calories.
        List under "Phosphorus" the grain products giving more
    than 0.05 gram of phosphorus per 100 Calories.

List under "Iron" the grain products giving more than 0.0005 gram of iron per 100 Calories. Combine these lists so that you have a list of at least five grain products rich in all three mineral elements.

Jack was very fond of the crisp, crunchy cereals, but the bulk eaten of most of these prepared cereals is likely to be insufficient to give the necessary food value; neither are they to be recommended as sources of iron, so that it is well to reserve them for variety, or for supper in the summer time.

Warm cooked cereals are to be preferred for a regular diet, as no extra heat is needed in warming the food taken into the stomach.

PROBLEM

67. With the aid of the data in your notebook from Problem 7, p. 30, make a chart similar to Chart XXIII in this chapter, showing the amount of energy obtained for the money spent for rolled oats, cornmeal, cornflakes, rice, farina, shredded wheat, and macaroni.

Jack learns to like oatmeal. When Jack's mother realized that oatmeal was much better for him than those cereals to which he was accustomed, she also remembered that oatmeal was his pet aversion. Nevertheless, a dish of it was placed before him. In surprise he pushed it away and confidently asked for something else. As his mother had learned that it is unwise to deceive children, she had been careful to wait before offering the oatmeal until she had no prepared cereal in the house, so that she could truthfully say she had none for him. Jack took this excuse as final the first morning, but preferred not to eat the oatmeal. His mother did not urge it, but gave him some whole wheat bread toast that was on the table. The next morning he was not so happy about the change, but, since he refused to eat the toast and milk and no substitute was offered, he had to go without breakfast. An hour later he was asking for a cookie and was somewhat surprised to see oatmeal and milk appear instead. As he did not want it, his mother did not urge it, but she did not give him anything in place of it. Jack was most unhappy for the rest of the morning, but at noon he had his regular dinner and forgot his sorrow. The next morning, without reference to what had previously happened, a little oatmeal was added to the milk to make "Tiny Bear grow big and strong like Tom." With a little firmness on the part of the mother it was eaten, and from then on the difficulty diminished and the amount eaten increased, until Jack was taking his full amount of three tablespoonfuls in the morning and the same quantity in the evening.

No sugar was added as a bribe, however. If children are taught from the first to eat cereal without sugar, they will not miss it, and there will not be a constant struggle to keep the amount within reason. What is most important, they will not tire of the unsweetened cereal as quickly as they will of cereal covered with sugar.

Cereal should be well cooked. Mrs. Irving found that all the children liked the cereal better when it had been cooked for a long time, and they would eat more of it if it was not too stiff. The long cooking improves the flavor. This is best accomplished by the use of a double boiler or by one saucepan set inside another, the outer one containing boiling water. It is frequently more convenient, and a saving in both time and money, to cook the cereal when the fire is being used for the cooking of other food, as in the evening or at noon. The cereal may then be reheated in the morning by setting the cereal kettle in a pan of hot water on the stove. Or, where the fire is kept during the night, the cereal may be cooked all night in a double boiler on the back of the range. In summer enough cereal may be cooked one day for two mornings, but care must be taken to keep the unused portion cold to prevent souring.

One of the best utensils for cooking cereal is the fireless cooker. Mrs. Irving had been in the habit of using one during the summer for tough meats, but when she found that the children liked the cereal better after it had been cooked for a long time, she began to use it in the winter as well. It was so easy to cook the cereal for fifteen minutes in the evening, put it in the cooker, and have it ready to serve in the morning without further thought.

PROBLEM

68. To review the cooking of cereals:

Cook cereals in a double boiler. Cook cereals in a fireless cooker. Serve the cereals in some attractive way which will appeal to a child as old as Jack.

What and how much cereal may be given? At the beginning of the third year, a child needs from one half to three fourths of a cupful or more of cereal, but this amount should be gradually increased to three fourths of a cupful or one cupful during the third and fourth years, the exact quantity depending on the size and activity of the child. If it seems difficult for a child to eat the required amount of cereal as mush for breakfast or supper, part of it may be put into soups or made into simple cereal puddings with any of the fruits mentioned on page 190. Raisins should be used cautiously, if at all, at this age, and, if used, they should be very thoroughly cooked and well chewed.

Bread furnishes exercise for teeth. When Mrs. Irving took Jack to the dentist for the semi-annual inspection of his teeth, the dentist told her that Jack's teeth, like his muscles, needed exercise to make and to keep them strong. As neither milk nor cereals require much chewing, these foods should be supplemented with a slice of day-old bread, a piece of zwieback, or a piece of toast at each meal, the size of the slice varying and increasing with the needs of the child. Any plain wholesome bread may be given, but if there is danger of iron or vitamin B deficiency, whole wheat bread will help to overcome it.

Homemade zwieback is to be preferred to that bought at the store, because it may be made less sweet. To make it, toast slices of ordinary bread in a moderate oven until of a golden brown throughout.

Fruit is very important. Mrs. Irving reasoned that fruit would be the easiest and surest means of introducing vitamin C into Jack's diet. And, since vitamin C is essential for health and since it is not stored in the tissues, she decided that fruit must be given daily to every member of her family.

By the beginning of the third year, a small amount

of almost any ripe fruit may be given to healthy children. It is well to have some uncooked citrus fruit daily, but it may be given every other day, especially if a green leafy vegetable is given on the days when no citrus fruit is served. Cooked fruit should not be very sweet. All fruit given should be in good condition. Decomposed or spoiled fruit is dangerous.

Value of vegetables. Vegetables should be given for their mineral elements and their vitamins, which stimulate and regulate the internal activities and help to preserve health. They also add bulk to the diet, which makes them useful in overcoming constipation. One cannot afford to do without them, both for the sake of health and for the sake of economy. Jack, who is three years old, should have two or three tablespoonfuls a day of each of two or more suitable vegetables, in addition to a potato every day.

Ways of serving vegetables. Mrs. Irving often disguised the vegetables by putting them in soup, where they were so finely mashed that no distinct particles could be seen. Sometimes, even then, Jack had to be persuaded to eat his soup "to see the butterfly on the bottom of the bowl." Sometimes a change in the way of serving added to the eagerness with which a vegetable was eaten. Oftentimes it was concealed in a scrambled egg or in milk toast, but very frequently the vegetables were given clear so that Jack might become accustomed to the taste. If he refused to eat any particular vegetable one day, his mother was sure to give him another taste of it a few days later, repeating it again and again, but never forcing him to eat it. When he became acquainted with the new taste, he would begin to swallow some of the vegetable, and so the habit of eating a variety grew, very, very slowly. Vegetables may be served in a variety of ways, but they should **never** be given **fried** to children.

SELECT ONE OR MORE VEGETABLES FROM EACH GROUP EACH DAY

Group I		Group II	
Asparagus	Escarole	Beans, dry (in soups)	Peas, dry (in soup)
Beet greens	Kale	Beets, young	
Cabbage	Lettuce	Carrots	Potatoes, white or sweet
Chard	String beans	Celery, cooked	
Dandelions	Turnip tops	Onions, young	Squash
Any other green leaf, cooked		Peas, young	Tomatoes
			Turnip, mild

All vegetables should be cooked for children until the end of the third year, when a little finely chopped raw carrot, cabbage, celery, spinach, lettuce, or white turnip may be given in a sandwich once or twice a week. Mineral elements and vitamins B and G are soluble in water and may be lost in the process of cooking; for this reason the occasional uncooked vegetable is a safety measure.

PROBLEM

69. To become familiar with the vegetables furnishing mineral elements in largest amounts:

Make a list of those vegetables 100 Calories of which contain more than 0.1 gram of calcium; make a list of those with more than 0.1 gram of phosphorus; make a list of those with more than 0.002 gram of iron.

At current prices, which vegetables will be the cheapest sources of iron?

Eggs. When Jack was a year old, Mrs. Irving had given him an egg one day, but it made him so ill she consulted the doctor, who told her that egg white frequently causes sickness in small children; the egg yolk is a safe food at any time, however. He told her not to give the egg white until Jack was three years old; then to test the reaction with only a taste the first day and if there were no ill effects to try a little larger amount two or three days later. Mrs. Irving had followed the doctor's advice, and she now felt safe in putting four or five whole eggs a week into Jack's diet.

Eggs furnish valuable protein; with the exception of cod-liver oil, they are the best known source of vitamin D; and they are rich in iron. They form a valuable part of the diet of growing children. It is possible, however, to eat too many eggs; it is seldom wise to eat more than one egg in any one day.

Eggs may be given in a variety of ways, such as soft-boiled, poached, coddled, scrambled, and in egg-nogs, but they should never be given fried to young children.

Cod-liver oil. For safety, Mrs. Irving continued the cod-liver oil for Jack through the preschool period. A teaspoonful three times a day was the dose. Although he was having four or five eggs a week, Mrs. Irving was afraid he might not have all the vitamins A and D a growing child needs to prevent colds and to build up a resistance to other infections of the respiratory tract. She was especially particular about giving the oil when the weather was too cold or stormy for Jack to play in the sunshine, for she recalled that cod-liver oil is sometimes called "bottled sunshine", and will serve practically the same purpose as the sun in aiding good development of bones and teeth and resistance in the tissues.

Meat is not a necessity. Meat is too stimulating for the majority of children, and is not necessary in the diet if a child has plenty of milk and some vegetables every day, especially if an egg is given every other day. The broth from meat may be used combined with vegetables and cereals, but the broth itself contains so little food value that there is no reason why the meat should be purchased for the sole purpose of making the broth.

Butter and Other Fats

Butter is a valuable food. Some fat is desirable for growing children. While butter is important because of its high energy value, it is much more important because of the vitamin A dissolved in it. Since the cream of whole milk is fully as valuable as the butter made from it, and since this food factor, A, is also in leafy vegetables, it is probable that the necessary amount of this growth-stimulator will be provided where a child is getting a whole quart of unskimmed milk with some green vegetable every day. Butter is, however, an agreeable and a desirable addition. Jack, in his third year, is allowed a tablespoonful of butter a day.

Other fats. No butter substitute is as rich in vitamin A as butter itself, but a good quality of either nut margarine or oleomargarine may be used in place of, or in addition to, butter, provided the diet contains a quart of milk per child per day, and a green leafy vegetable. Mrs. Irving added a piece of crisp bacon or a teaspoonful of olive or salad oil occasionally to increase the energy content of Jack's diet, but she remembered that fat retards digestion and that for this reason it should be added to the diet of a child very cautiously.

Sugars and sweets. Jack had already acquired a sweet tooth, for, as you know, this harmful habit is easily formed during these early years; but when his

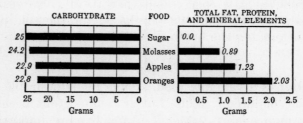

Chart XXIV. — Relative food value in 100-Calorie portions of sugar, molasses, and some fruits

mother learned of the danger of eating too much sweet food, she began to guard against it.

Sugar and sweets are valuable because of the concentrated energy they contain, but, at the same time, they have very few other good qualities. For this reason there is grave danger of receiving so much of the daily energy requirement from sweets that the growing materials will be deficient. Tables XXII, XXIII, XXIV, XXV, and XXVI show how little protein, calcium, phosphorus, and iron are contained in sugar, honey, and syrups.

Chart XXIV represents the value of sugar compared with that of molasses, apples, and oranges. It is better to obtain the energy from such foods, for at the same time mineral elements and vitamins will be added to the diet. Brown sugar also contains a little more food value than white sugar and is to be recommended in place of it. It is better not to put sugar on cereal, as it is much more wholesome for a child to acquire a taste for the cereal itself. A three-year-old may have a little jelly or molasses, but the amount of all sweets given should not be more than one to two tablespoonfuls a day during the third and fourth years; any amount of sugar given is best used in dilute form, as in cooked foods, although one piece of candy at the end of a meal once or twice a week is permissible.

Forbidden Foods for Children from One to Five Years of Age

Tea, coffee, strong cocoa, or chocolate

All fried foods, including griddlecakes, doughnuts, and fried potatoes

Raw vegetables, such as cucumbers and radishes

All green or spoiled fruit

All hot breads, pies, pastry, and rich cake

Frosted cookies and cake

All rich puddings and sauces

All pickles, sweet preserves, and nuts

All strong spice and vinegar

Canned, dried, and salted meat or fish and pork (except crisp bacon)

Game, sausage, frankfurters, and bologna

All candy except at the end of a meal

TABLE XXXIV. — MEALS FOR A CHILD DURING THE FOURTH YEAR
1100 TO 1400 CALORIES (35 to 40 Calories per pound)

| Food | Quantity | | Calories | Protein |
	Amount	Weight		
		Ounces		*Grams*
Breakfast:				
7:00–7:30 A.M.				
Cereal	¾ cupful	7.2 (0.75 oz., dry)	90	3.8
Milk for cereal and for drinking . .	1½ cupfuls	12.0	240	12.0
Bread	1 slice	0.7	50	1.8
Butter	1 tsp.	0.15	33	. .
Fruit	3 tbsp.	1.5 (average)	18 (average)	. .
Dinner:				
11:30 A.M.–12:00 M.				
Egg, fish, cottage cheese, or bean or pea soup . .			75 (average)	4.2 (average)
Potato	1 medium	4.2	100	2.8
Other vegetables .	5 tbsp.	4.4	28	. .
Milk	1 cupful	8.0	160	8.0
Bread	1½ slices	1.0	75	2.7
Butter	½ tbsp.	0.23	50	. .
Plain dessert [1] . .	⅓ cupful	3.6 (average)	50 (average)	2.5 (average)
Supper:				
5:30–6 P.M.				
Cereal	¾ cupful	7.2 (0.75 oz., dry)	90	3.8
Milk	1 cupful	8.0	160	8.0
Bread	1 slice	0.7	50	1.8
Butter	1 tsp.	0.15	33	. .
Cooked fruit . .	3 tbsp.	1.8	50 (average)	. .
Totals	. . . .	. . . .	1352	51.4

[1] For desserts, serve custards, junket, tapioca, gelatin dessert, stewed
fruit, or cereal puddings, such as rice, farina, or cornstarch

TABLE XXXV. — MEALS FOR A CHILD DURING THE FIFTH YEAR
1200 TO 1500 CALORIES   (33 to 37 Calories per pound)

| FOOD | QUANTITY | | CALORIES | PROTEIN |
	AMOUNT	WEIGHT		
		Ounces		Grams
Breakfast: 7:00 to 7:30 A.M.				
Cereal	¾ cupful	7.2 (0.75 oz., dry)	90	3.8
Milk for drinking and for cereal .	1½ cupfuls	12.0	240	12.0
Bread	2 slices	1.4	100	3.6
Butter	½ tbsp.	0.23	50	..
Fruit	4 tbsp.	2.0 (average)	24	..
Dinner: 11:30 A.M.–12:00 M.				
Egg, fish, cottage cheese, or bean or pea soup . .			75 (average)	4.2 (average)
Potato	1 medium	4.2	100	2.8
Other vegetables .	6 tbsp.	5.2	34	..
Milk	1 cupful	8.0	160	8.0
Bread	2 slices	1.4	100	3.6
Butter	½ tbsp.	0.23	50	..
Plain dessert [1] .	⅓ cupful	3.6 (average)	50 (average)	2.5
Supper: 5:30–6:00 P.M.				
Cereal	¾ cupful	7.2 (0.75 oz., dry)	90	3.8
Milk	1 cupful	8.0	160	8.0
Egg (if not given at noon), creamed vegetable, or a little dessert .			40 (average)	2.0 (average)
Bread	1 slice	0.7	50	1.8
Butter	½ tbsp.	0.23	50	..
Total			1463	56.1

[1] Custards, junkets, cornstarch pudding, gelatin, stewed fruit and plain cookies, tapioca, floating island, rice or farina pudding

Good Habits Help Good Food to Build Strong Bodies

The way in which food is eaten and the habits of rest, sleep, exercise, and play in the sunshine are almost as important as good food. Jack was unfortunate for many reasons. Both his food and his habits of rest and exercise were wrong. His good fortune lay in the fact that his mother realized his danger before it was too late. He had been eating fruit and sweets between meals; he drank very little water; he had been bolting his food and rushing off to play; he had been sitting up after seven o'clock at night; and he took no rests during the day. After his habits were regulated, he had nothing except water between meals; he ate slowly; he had a nap each day; his elimination was more regular; he went to bed early; he had his bedroom windows open so as to get fresh air while sleeping; and he was out of doors much more during the day. His finicky appetite soon gave way to one ready for whatever was placed before him, his disposition improved, and he was much less nervous; Jack was brighter and livelier than ever.

PROBLEMS

70. Following the schedule in Table XXXIII, prepare the day's meals for a child of three years.

71. Following the schedule in Table XXXV, prepare the day's meals for a child of five years.

72. Compare the meals prepared in Problems 70 and 71 with those you have seen children of the same age eating.

QUESTIONS

1. What did Mrs. Irving learn from the experiments which had been made with rats at Yale University?

2. Discuss the schedule that Mrs. Irving prepared for Jack's diet.

3. What continues to be the basis of the diet of children from two up to five years of age? If children grow tired of milk, or think they do not like it, suggest methods of keeping this food in the diet.

4. How would you teach a child to eat cereals when he thinks he does not like them?

5. Do children usually object to eating fruit? When and how should fruit be given to children between two and five years of age?

6. What problem do eggs present? Why are they so valuable in the diet of children?

7. Discuss the advisability of including meat in the diet of children from two to five years of age.

8. How may food habits control constipation?

9. What are the dangers of too many sweets in the diet?

10. Completion test:

    A child's health is influenced by his —— —— of eating.

    Children of three years of age should have —— meals a day.

    Toast or zwieback is given to children to —— their teeth.

    Besides potato, children need —— tablespoonfuls of —— other vegetables daily. One of these vegetables should be a —— —— vegetable.

REFERENCES

For students:

PETERS, L. H., M.D. *Diet for Children*. Dodd, Mead, and Company (1924).

ROSE, MARY S. *Feeding the Family*, third edition, Chapter VII. The Macmillan Company (1929).

For teachers:

BARNES, MRS. H. F. *Feeding the Child from Two to Six*. The Macmillan Company (1928).

LUCAS, W. P., M.D. *The Health of the Runabout Child*. The Macmillan Company (1923).

ROSE, MARY S. *Foundations of Nutrition*. The Macmillan Company (1927).

Pamphlets from the Infant Welfare Society (404 South 8th Street, Minneapolis): *How to Get Children to Eat Vegetables; How to Get Children to Drink Milk; How to Get Children to Eat Cereals and Fruits*.

CHAPTER XII

FOOD FOR SCHOOL CHILDREN AND ADULTS

EVERY normal child and adult needs milk, vegetables, fruit, and fat. Therefore it is not difficult to plan breakfast, midday, and evening meals satisfactory for the whole family, even though each has his individual Calorie and other food requirement.

If soups, vegetables, and desserts are simply prepared and served with plenty of milk, eggs, bread, butter, and cereals for children and elderly people, adults will not have to forego entirely the pleasure of more elaborate dishes.

DICK AND CLARE IRVING

Dick, it will be remembered, was seven years old. We also recall that he was very fond of coffee, that he frequently drank it in place of milk, that he ate much meat and few vegetables, and that he sat up late at night, thus violating some of the fundamental laws of health. As a result, his weight was below the lower limit of the safety zone.

Clare, who was ten years old, was a joy to all her friends because of her untiring energy, her sparkling good health, and her contagious good nature. Her companions singled her out as the most welcome member of any group. She was quite a contrast to Dick in both health and habits, particularly food habits. She liked milk and vegetables, cared little for meat, and never touched coffee. The teacher at school had told them that coffee was not good for growing children and might result in malnutrition, which would be a great hindrance at some critical time when they would like to do especially good work. As Clare had ambitions for a life of useful service, she did not want to run any risks. Although the good-natured jests of the rest of the family oftentimes tempted her to try to sit up after half past eight o'clock at night, wise nature usually protected her by causing her to fall asleep over her books. Then she was up bright and early the next morning and had her lessons prepared in about half the time it would have taken her the night before.

THE REST OF THE IRVING FAMILY

Mr. and Mrs. Irving. Mr. and Mrs. Irving were in the early forties. They considered themselves in fairly good physical condition, though Mr. Irving had frequent colds and was extremely tired every night. Mrs. Irving was troubled with headache occasionally, and she also tired easily; her weight was considerably above the upper limit of the safety zone, but only recently had it occurred to her that it might be controlled through diet.

Grandma Irving. Grandma Irving ate as heartily as ever, but she lived a quiet life without much physical exercise. She helped with such sitting-down work as sewing, shelling beans and peas, cleaning beet greens, and paring potatoes, when these were to be used in such a way as to justify the removal of the skins. She was always jolly and interested in whatever the children were doing and seemed in good health, except that she did not sleep very well and often had a distressed feeling after eating.

When she heard Mrs. Irving and the children talking about the relation of food to health, she laughingly asked whether the books said anything about diet for elderly people. Alice investigated and found that since people are inclined to exercise less vigorously after forty or fifty years of age, their food needs are usually less; also that the processes which maintain life (heart beat, circulation, digestion, and the functions of all other organs) gradually become slower as one grows older, thus making it impossible for the body to use the same amount of food as previously. If the amount of food eaten is not reduced, there is danger of injury to internal organs.

Grandma Irving was quick to understand, and she saw at once how unreasonable it was for her to continue to eat as much as had been her custom when she was more active. She wondered, also, whether fried foods, rich cakes and pastries, doughnuts, and other similar indiscretions might be responsible for her sleeplessness; and, since her digestion was slower, the eating of such foods might easily explain that distressed feeling she often had after eating. Her desire to keep herself in good condition as long as possible prompted her to study her own needs more thoroughly.

Mrs. Irving's Whole Problem

May the same meal be satisfactory for both children and adults? Mrs. Irving's problem consisted of the preparation of three meals a day, each of which must be adapted to a group of nine people, made up of six children of various ages with different Calorie and other food requirements, of two middle-aged adults, and an elderly person. The food must appeal to the finicky and fickle appetite of Alice and, at the same time, satisfy that huge and undiscriminating desire for food which Tom had; it must be simple and easily digestible for Betty, Jack, Dick, and grandma; it must enable Mr. Irving to maintain his weight, strength, and endurance; and it must help Mrs. Irving to reduce her weight but at the same time increase her resistance. The diet must be such as to prevent or to overcome constipation for several members of the family.

Many of Mrs. Irving's friends said they had no time in which to prepare extra food for the various members of their respective families, but Mrs. Irving was willing and anxious to do all she could to make her children well and strong, and she was sure she could find a solution.

Mrs. Irving's solution. She reasoned that the foods prohibited in the diet of a child after the fifth year are so few that there is no reason why the same meals cannot be planned to provide for the needs of the whole family, or for all those over five years of age. There must, of course, be some exceptions for the very young children, but even their meals may be such as to reduce the extra work to a very small amount.

Milk, vegetables, fruit, and fat are fundamental for both children and adults. These foods may or may not be supplemented with meat. Even though meat is served for the older members, the rest of the meal must be such that Jack, Dick, and Grandma Irving may have adequate nourishment without it. If potatoes, bread, cereals, and other starchy foods are included in the menu, those who must maintain or gain weight may eat liberal amounts of them, while grandma and Mrs. Irving may use them sparingly or omit them entirely if they think best. Sweets should be used cautiously by everyone. Then, obviously, these foods, provided they are properly prepared, will offer no insurmountable barrier in the planning of meals appropriate for the whole family.

Three meals a day. Mrs. Irving also knew that the foods named must be served in three substantial and nourishing meals a day; namely, breakfast, a midday meal, and an evening meal, with no eating between meals unless specially advised and planned.

Breakfast should be served early enough to allow time for proper mastication and for the eating of a sufficient amount to furnish energy for the morning and some material for growth in addition. The breakfast for Dick and Clare should be similar in make-up to that described for Jack, with quantities of bread, butter, and cereals somewhat increased according to age and activity.

The books that Mrs. Irving read said that the luncheon for growing children is as important and needs as much careful thought as the other two meals of the day. It should consist of a quantity of such easily digestible foods as will provide enough nourishment to prevent fatigue during the afternoon. It should be prepared so that it may be quickly eaten to avoid the swallowing of half-chewed food. Jack's midday meal made a very appropriate foundation for the luncheon of Dick and Clare.

The evening meal must necessarily be the heartiest meal of the day for Dick, Clare, and Mr. Irving, because they did not have time in which to eat a more substantial meal at noontime. While Mrs. Irving realized that it would be better for Dick and Clare to have the most nourishing meal at noon, the Irvings lived too far from school to make this possible, but she said: "If the evening meal contains milk, properly prepared vegetables, plenty of bread and butter or cereals, and simple desserts, the children may have a satisfactory dinner without much meat or other forbidden things."

Mrs. Irving was convinced she could adapt her three meals to each of the nine members of her family. In addition to the serving of the right food, she was quite decided that each meal should be free from hurry, worry, unkind words, anger, nagging, and undue excitement, for she had read that these things interfere with good digestion.

FOODS APPLIED TO THE NEEDS OF SCHOOL CHILDREN AND ADULTS

Milk is necessary for both children and adults. Milk is still the best and most important food throughout the period of growth. There is no substitute for it and no food just as good. Every child and every adult (including young men and women, the middle-aged, and the elderly) ought to have at least a pint of milk daily, and a quart is better, especially for children. It may be given as plain milk to drink, or it may be prepared in some cooked form, such as cocoa, soups, and puddings.

As Mrs. Irving had learned through her study of her family food problems that no other food can supply satisfactorily the calcium needed for the proper development and up-keep of bones and teeth, and for the control of the various activities which make life possible, she planned the meals so that each member of her family should receive at least a pint a day in some cooked form; and then, without asking Dick whether he wanted it or not, she insisted that he drink another two cups. Tea and coffee were now forbidden. At first, Dick had a headache without the stimulant, but this disappeared at the end of a week, and the change from coffee to milk marked the first step in his improvement. Strange to say, he began to like milk when he found how much more pep he had because of it. It was unnecessary to urge Clare to drink milk, because she was very fond of it and had always had a quart a day. Mr. and Mrs. Irving still felt they must have their tea and coffee, but, even so, it meant no extra work to set glasses of milk on the table for the children.

Milk may be used in so many different ways, such as milk soups, creamed dishes, and desserts, that Mrs. Irving found no difficulty in incorporating in her meals the full amount planned. When she ran out of fresh milk or sometimes even though she had fresh milk, she would use unsweetened evaporated milk in cocoa and desserts. The children liked the change, it was cheaper, and therefore a wise move for any thrifty housewife. Mrs. Irving was so delighted with the idea that she told many of her friends about it when they said they could not afford milk because it added to the expense of their meals. She also explained to them that milk is the last food item to be omitted from the diet of children; meat may be reduced with very much less harm than milk. In reality, Dick ate less meat when he had the milk, and he felt better too.

Cheese. Cheese has most of the good qualities of milk in a condensed form. Cream or cottage cheese was given to Betty occasionally for variety, and these soft cheeses on bread and crackers made nice sandwiches to serve with vegetable soups at luncheon for the school children. A pound of hard cheese has the food value of from six to eight pounds of milk. Hard cheese is very concentrated and should be given to children only after it has been combined with other foods in such a way that it will not be swallowed in large pieces. One of the best ways of serving it is to melt it in white sauce and combine it with cooked rice, macaroni, or potato. It becomes objectionable only when sprinkled on the top of a dish and browned or baked in the oven until the cheese becomes tough and stringy.

PROBLEMS

73. Plan a day's meals for Dick with one half quart of milk concealed in cooked food.

74. Plan a day's meals for the Irving family, using in cooked food one pint of milk for each member of the family. Prepare the dishes in which milk is used.

75. To compare the cost of milk and meat:
    Plan two meals of 1500 Calories each, one to include 4 to 6 ounces of meat, the other with an equivalent number of Calories from milk. Calculate the difference in cost.

Bread, cereals, and other grain products. As Dick's mother wanted him to have the advantage of the whole grain, she insisted that he eat oatmeal, wheatena, pettijohn's, ralston, malt breakfast food, and other similar cereals from which the outer coating has not been removed, to obtain a maximum of nourishment in a minimum of bulk. Dick did not like the change from cornflakes to a cooked cereal any better than Jack had, but when he rebelled his mother asked him if he wanted Jack to show him how a man should act, whereupon his seven years prompted him to set Jack a good example. Have you ever realized how much influence the older brothers and sisters have on the likes and dislikes of the younger children?

As whole grain cereals are better for the other members of the family, both because of their mineral elements and vitamins, and because they help to prevent constipation, only whole grain cereals were served in the Irving family from that time forward. Since practically any well-cooked cereal may be given after the second year, the only difference in the serving of the cereal for the various members of the Irving family lay in the quantity each required.

The quantity of bread and cereal any person should eat will depend on the amount of energy or the number of Calories needed. As Dick must gain in weight. his mother encouraged him to eat at least two slices of bread at each meal. Tom, who was growing rapidly, needed several slices. Mrs. Irving was very fond of both bread and cereals, but she decided to omit cereals entirely until her weight was reduced to the amount she should have weighed at age thirty and to eat whole wheat toast with her coffee in the morning. Grandma Irving thought cereal would be better for her at breakfast time than the toast, so she decided to omit the bread in the morning but to use it as toast with her tea in the afternoon. Mr. Irving needed generous amounts of both bread and cereals to maintain weight, strength, and endurance. Again Mrs. Irving said: "Bread, like milk, offers no problem in the serving of meals for my family. I will put the bread on the table and each may eat as much or as little as he needs or likes."

PROBLEM

76. Plan a day's meals for Dick in which about one third of the energy will be supplied by bread or other grain products. Add enough Calories from the same sources to make the meal adequate for Tom.

The one difficulty in the Irving family. Both Mr. and Mrs. Irving had been brought up where hot breads and fried cereals were often served. They were still very fond of them, but they realized that these foods should not be given to children. To omit them was going to be a hardship, yet to have them meant extra work in the preparation of meals for both children and adults.

Mrs. Irving put the following questions up to the older members of the family:

1. Is the health of the children of more importance than the pleasure of the adult?
2. Shall we deny ourselves for the sake of the children?
3. Shall I prepare extra things for the children?

They decided as follows: first, that the children must not have foods that were not good for them; second, that they themselves would be content with fried foods a little less frequently; and, third, that when fried foods were to be served for the adults something else must be prepared for the children. Grandma Irving felt that it would be better for her to eat no more fried foods, for she felt sure they had been partly responsible for her stomach trouble of late. Thereafter, when Mr. and Mrs. Irving had fried mush, the children and their grandmother had cereal and cooked dried fruit molded in a cup and served with syrup or molasses. Mrs. Irving sometimes gave them raisin bread when the rest of the family were having griddle-cakes. As the raisin bread was not served at other times, it was a real treat. Or perhaps she made toast, spread it with a little jelly, and moistened it with hot milk. But, since these things took extra time, more than she wanted to spend, gradually she and her husband had fried foods less frequently, and they felt better for the change.

PROBLEM

77. If there were children under 12 years of age in your own home and if your family were in the habit of eating fried mush, fried cakes, fried meats, fried eggs, hot breads, rich pies and cakes, and heavy salads, how would you arrange to substitute other foods for the children or to prepare these same foods in a manner suitable for them to eat?

Vegetables should be eaten freely by everyone. To increase the mineral and vitamin content of the diet of the family and to provide foods that would help to prevent constipation, Mrs. Irving planned to use a green leafy vegetable, such as spinach, chard, dandelions, beet and turnip tops, lettuce, celery, cabbage, Brussels sprouts, asparagus, and cauliflower at least once a day, potatoes once or twice a day, and at least one other vegetable.

Children may eat vegetables cooked in almost any way except fried or otherwise cooked in fat, and when Mrs. Irving enumerated all the various ways in which vegetables may be served — plain boiled with or without butter, mashed, baked, creamed, escalloped, in soups, stews, and salads — she realized that the preparation of vegetables presented no problem in the planning of meals for the whole family.

One of the chief difficulties was in persuading Dick and Alice to eat lettuce and other green leaves when served as a part of the salad, but when her mother reminded Alice how essential were the food constituents in green leaves, she ate even the parsley with which the potatoes and meats were occasionally adorned.

Vegetables are among the important supports of a healthy and vigorous life. Clare had unconsciously laid a good foundation for health by eating vegetables, while Dick had been slowly drifting away from it by refusing to eat them. When Mrs. Irving took special care to prepare them in attractive ways, Dick began to acquire a taste for them which was a very important factor in stimulating his strength to return; and with returning strength came an increasing appetite, to which just plain boiled vegetables eventually appealed.

By the end of the fifth year the variety of vegetables allowed is so great that it is much easier to enumerate the ones to be avoided than those that may be used. Cucumbers are usually forbidden to children entirely, so they may be dismissed without further comment. Cabbage and corn should be given very cautiously before the twelfth year. If properly cooked it is probable that the chief dangers from these vegetables are in eating too much of them, in eating them in too concentrated a form, and in not chewing them thoroughly.

Cabbage is useful because of its vitamins and iron and other mineral elements, and, if properly cooked, it may be given to children three and four years of age. Some of the ill effects which may be felt from the eating of cabbage are due to the fat with which it is often cooked. The fat retards digestion and allows fermentation, which results in irritation and distress. Cabbage for children should be cooked in clear, salted water without salt pork, fat, oil, or other fat; it should be cooked only until tender and served with a little butter.

Mrs. Irving had a way of preparing the corn that made it possible for children seven years old and over to eat small amounts of it. She scraped out the juicy inner part of the kernel in such a way as to leave the outside part remaining on the cob. This was done by cutting the kernels through the middle of each row and scraping out the inside with a knife. With milk and seasoning the corn was then cooked in a double boiler for at least a half hour. Corn prepared in this way is better for both adults and children. Grandma Irving also appreciated this method of cooking corn because she had difficulty in eating the corn from the cob. She was eating more vegetables of all kinds since the children were talking about them; as a result her elimination was better, she had more ambition to take a walk out of doors each day, and she felt better.

Mrs. Irving naturally ate more green vegetables as she reduced the amount of bread, cereals, and potato; she ate a moderate amount of potato because she must have some energy and she also wanted the basic effect which comes from the eating of this vegetable, but she left bread and cereals almost entirely alone. She soon found that she was less easily exhausted and had fewer headaches. Mr. Irving remarked that he was feeling more energetic than he had in ten years, and Mrs. Irving and the children wondered whether milk and vegetables might have something to do with the return of his former jolly self.

PROBLEM

78. Plan the vegetables for the Irving family for a week. Distribute them according to days. Include potatoes at least once every day, a leafy vegetable every day, and a root vegetable several times during the week. Consider season, cost, and adaptability to both children and adults.

Fruit is easily provided. All the Irving children were very fond of fruit, and, because of the way in which fruit is usually served, it was very simple for their mother to introduce all the fruit which seemed advisable for them. Mrs. Irving was conscious that each child and grown person should have either some fresh citrus fruit, some tomato, or a raw, green leafy vegetable every day, for the purpose of providing vitamin C. As the children were very fond of apples, pears, peaches, and other fruit, their mother took the opportunity of, and felt safe in, serving these fruits on the days when she had tomatoes as a vegetable or when she served a raw, green leafy vegetable salad.

Jams and jellies are better sources of energy than fresh fruit, but they are so sweet there is danger that they may spoil the appetite for other foods; it is probable, also, that fruit in these forms does not contain much vitamin C, and it is unwise to use these foods in place of fresh fruit.

Eggs. Eggs are such a valuable food for children and are usually so acceptable to adults that Mrs. Irving planned to serve eggs at least four or five times a week, but she was warned against giving more than one egg in any one day to Dick and Clare, who were not yet twelve years of age. Eggs may be given to children in a variety of ways; in fact, children may have them cooked in any way except fried. Since they are almost always cooked in such a way as to admit of individual choice, they do not complicate the planning of meals for either children or adults.

Meat, fish, and fowl. If the diet contains plenty of vegetables and milk, and especially if eggs are used, meat is not necessary for the majority of either children or adults. A little meat or fish before the seventh year will not be injurious, however, but the quantity given should not exceed an ounce a day. Dick should not have more than two ounces a day before he is ten years old; Clare should have not over three ounces before she is as old as Alice; while Alice and Tom ought not to have over four ounces a day. With both meat and vegetables served at the same meal, the children and grandma may have a small amount of meat and a generous quantity of vegetables.

PROBLEM

79. How much meat would you consider a fair allowance for the Irving family for one day? How much milk? Compare the cost of your estimates.

Sweets had better be reduced to a small amount for both children and adults. Sugar is a good food in its place, but when eaten between meals it takes away the appetite for better foods. Of all bad food habits to overcome perhaps a "sweet tooth" is the hardest. Poor Dick! He seemed to have been committing every dietetic sin. He was very fond of candy and quite often ate it between meals. When his mother refused to let him have it except at the end of his meals, he had a very annoying craving for it. He was encouraged to eat more bread and cereals at breakfast and dinner; he was given an occasional piece of fruit in the middle of the morning because that sudden withdrawal of an immediate source of energy made him feel faint; and he was told to drink plenty of water. In time the craving wore off and the normal appetite returned.

The craving for something sweet may be natural, but nature does not furnish pure sugar or candy. The natural way to satisfy the craving for sweet is to eat sweet fruits. This is much better than eating sugar or candy, because the fruits furnish mineral elements and vitamins as well as sugar. Sugar, as we see it, contains neither mineral elements nor vitamins, and if too much of the energy is obtained from it, there is danger of a deficiency of some one of these elements.

Fat is needed by everyone. Fat is an excellent source of energy, but, as it can be used freely for this purpose only by those who can digest it easily, Grandma Irving, Dick, Jack, and Betty were given only small amounts of fatty foods.

For safety, Mrs. Irving preferred to serve butter for the children's bread because of its vitamin A content even though this food factor was probably amply provided through milk and green vegetables daily. Other oils, such as cottonseed, olive, corn, and peanut, are all good sources of energy, but, with the possible exception of corn oil, they do not contain any important amount of this growth-promoting substance. They may be used in addition to butter, but not in place of it, unless each child has a quart of milk and a green leafy vegetable every day.

Nuts. In general, the food value of nuts is high, and Mr. Irving, who was very fond of them, ate them freely; but Grandma Irving, Jack, Dick, and Clare were not allowed to eat nuts containing much fat. Tom had difficulty in digesting any nuts because he did not take the time to chew them thoroughly or because he ate them at a time when that distressed feeling in the stomach is its only way of saying that it is already overworked.

With the exception of peanut butter, children under seven years of age ought not to be allowed to eat nuts, both because they will not chew them carefully and because nuts with much fat may be hard to digest.

Peanut butter, which is already finely ground, may be used in moderation by children five years old.

Water is highly recommended. Water is very important and should be taken freely between meals by both children and adults. In the majority of cases, there is no reason why water may not be taken with meals, but it should not be used to wash food down. One or two cups at mealtime probably helps digestion, provided the drinking of water does not take the place of the chewing of food. Water is absolutely essential and the advice of all physicians is to drink plenty of it.

Good habits other than food. In addition to good, nourishing food, Dick and Clare need from ten to twelve hours of sleep each night, good posture, exercise, and play in the sunshine. Because Dick was underweight and had too many colds during the winter, his mother thought it best to give him cod-liver oil from the first of October until the first of April or May. She also took Dick and Clare to the doctor for a yearly physical examination, and to the dentist twice each year to have any small cavities discovered and filled before they became large enough to ache or to destroy the teeth.

PROBLEMS

80. Plan a day's meals for Dick and Clare conforming to the foregoing suggestions. Prepare these meals. Would they be suitable meals for girls and boys of your age? If not, how might they be modified to make them so?

81. Plan and cook a Sunday dinner for the Irving family suitable in all respects for children and adults.

An Anti-Constipation Diet

Constipation is dangerous. There should be regular daily bowel movements to rid the body of waste material which accumulates in the intestines. Otherwise, poisonous products will be formed, absorbed from the intestines, and carried to all parts of the body, where they will lower resistance and make the tissues less able to cope with disease.

Some of the minor effects of constipation are headaches, dizziness, indigestion, a languid feeling, and a muddy complexion. Slight as these may seem, they may be the forerunners of serious illness.

Drugs. Drugs provide a temporary relief but not a permanent cure. Oftentimes, the quantity of drug taken has to be gradually increased until finally it becomes ineffective altogether. Drugs should be used only when recommended by a doctor.

Exercise. Regular exercise is more effective and lasting than drugs and should be taken daily. Walking, tennis, basketball, rowing, and skating are all helpful.

Water is invaluable. Water assists in overcoming constipation by keeping food in a semifluid state, and helps to carry poisonous products out of the system through the kidneys. Everyone, but especially those troubled with constipation, should drink from six to eight glasses of water a day.

Kinds of constipation. There are several causes of constipation. One form is the result of eating too little coarse food, while another form is caused and increased by the use of foods that are too stimulating, such as coarse cereals, bran, bulky vegetables, fruit skins, and the like. When constipation is caused or increased by these foods, it is best to have expert advice as to the means of overcoming it.

For the type of constipation that is caused by too little stimulation, use whole grain cereals (use bran cautiously), plenty of vegetables, and fruit at least once a day. Figs at bedtime and orange juice one half hour before breakfast are often useful. Molasses, honey, butternuts, baked beans, cabbage, onions, and the skins of baked potatoes are all helpful. Tea, coffee, candy, sweets, and rich pastries should be avoided.

PROBLEM

82. Plan a diet for a person who is troubled with constipation caused by eating too few foods containing bulk and by drinking insufficient water.

FACTS WHICH HELPED MRS. IRVING IN REDUCING

Overweight is dangerous. Overweight is dangerous because it means more work for heart and kidneys and greater danger of disease. Excessive weight is the result of too little exercise, of too much food, or of some physical condition. Before reducing measures are tried, there should be a physical examination, and if any physical abnormalities are found, reducing should be done only under the direction of a physician.

If overweight is due to insufficient exercise or excessive food, naturally the best remedy is a reduction in the amount of food and an increase in the amount of exercise, thus causing the body to burn its own fat for energy. If increased exercise stimulates the appetite, bulky vegetables and fruits will provide a minimum of energy while satisfying the craving for food.

Fatty tissue will be used for energy when the Calorie content of the diet is less than the energy needed by the individual. But the chief caution to observe in reducing Calories is to maintain protein, mineral elements, and vitamins to keep up resistance and the proper functioning of all the internal processes. These food factors, however, need to be supplied in proportion to normal weight, not in proportion to overweight. For example, a woman twenty-five years of age, 5 feet and 4 inches in height, weighing 250 pounds, needs protein for 125 pounds, the average weight for her height and age, rather than for her present weight.

It is unnecessary to omit entirely any one food, but all foods high in energy should be used cautiously (as bread, cereals, rice, macaroni and other grain products, potatoes, butter, cream, oil, sweets, and those dishes containing much fat, sugar, and starch). Food should be taken at regular hours, with no extras between meals, such as candy, sodas, sweet chocolate, nuts, cakes, cookies, or crackers.

Too much water should be avoided, as it tends to increase the appetite. Salt should be avoided, as it creates thirst.

For an overweight person whose normal requirement is from 2200 to 2700 Calories per day, Calories may be cautiously reduced to 1500, with milk, vegetables, and fruits predominating in the diet.

It is well to remember that from 200 to 300 Calories

more a day than the amount required to maintain weight and to provide for activity, will add weight at the rate of one half ounce a day, from four to eight ounces a week, and from one to two pounds a month. An hour of vigorous exercise will take care of an extra 100 or 200 Calories and perhaps burn some body tissue in addition.

PROBLEM

83. Plan a reducing diet for a girl fifteen years of age who is 30 pounds overweight, whose normal food requirement is 2200 Calories, and who probably has been eating 3200 Calories.

HINTS ON GAINING WEIGHT

Underweight is often accompanied by easy fatigue and lowered resistance and may lead to sickness. It may be due to physical defects, past or present illness, overfatigue, worry, too much of the wrong food, or too little of the right food. Too little fresh air and sunshine may keep a person who is eating even the best of diets from gaining. Worry, tension, and excitement may cause one person to lose weight on the same amount of food on which another will gain. Sweets between meals often destroy the appetite for vegetables and milk and thus rob the system of growing material, without which there is no gain.

The remedies are long hours of rest and sleep, fresh air and sunshine, freedom from worry and too much excitement, the correction of all physical defects (such as diseased or enlarged tonsils and adenoids, carious teeth, and bad posture), with a diet providing Calories somewhat above requirement and protein, mineral elements, and vitamins adequate for normal weight. Food needs are best supplied each day by a quart of milk, generous amounts of potatoes, green leafy vegetables, and at least one other vegetable, some fresh fruit, and whole grain cereals. In addition to the Calories provided by the above mentioned foods, the Calories may be further increased through a liberal use of bread, a moderate amount of fat, and a small amount of sugar. It is best to use fat and sugar cautiously as they may interfere with digestion and thus retard gains in weight.

PROBLEM

84. Plan a fattening diet for a girl fifteen years of age who is 30 pounds underweight, whose normal food requirement is 2200 Calories, and who has been in the habit of eating only 1500 Calories per day.

QUESTIONS

1. What health habits had Dick Irving been violating? How had this carelessness affected his health?

2. In what way did Clare Irving's health habits differ from Dick's? How had this affected her health and her popularity?

3. What led Grandma Irving to take a special interest in her food? How did Alice help her?

4. Discuss the problem which confronted Mrs. Irving in planning meals suitable for both children and adults.

5. Enumerate some of the plans Mrs. Irving made which helped her in the solution of her problem.

6. What food still forms the basis of the meals of the family? Why is cheese such a valuable food?

7. What kind of cereals did Mrs. Irving decide would be best to serve to the entire family? How did she determine the amount of bread each should eat?

8. Why is it so important that at least once a day everyone eat a green leafy salad? Do you always eat the lettuce served with your salad?

9. Explain why fresh fruits are more valuable in the diet than jams and jellies.

10. Discuss the advisability of substituting other fats for butter in the diet of a child.

11. Completion test:

Every adult should have at least —— —— of milk in his diet each day.

Butter is needed in the diet of each child to supply vitamin ——, unless the diet contains —— —— of milk and a —— vegetable.

Children under —— should —— have nuts in their diets.

The time to serve candy to adults or children is —— —— of a meal.

REFERENCES

For students:

Dowd, M. T. and Jameson, J. J. *Food and Its Preparation*, revised edition, Chapters V to XVIII. John Wiley & Son (1925).

Harris, J. W. and Lacey, E. V. *Everyday Foods*, Unit Four, Chapter XXIII. Houghton Mifflin Company (1927).

Rose, Mary S. *Feeding the Family*, third edition, Chapters VIII to XII. The Macmillan Company (1929).

For teachers:

Rose, Mary S. *Foundations of Nutrition*, Chapters XI and XII. The Macmillan Company (1927).

Sherman, H. C. *Chemistry of Food and Nutrition*, third edition, Chapter XXII. The Macmillan Company (1926).

CHAPTER XIII

PLANNING THE MEALS FOR A FAMILY

MEALS should be planned to provide daily for each person:

From one pint to one quart of milk, with one other protein dish

Two or more vegetables, with potatoes and green leafy vegetables well represented

Fruit, fresh or dried, with citrus fruit often

Grain products, fats, and sugars to make Calories adequate (fats and sugars to be used sparingly)

Mrs. Irving found the planning of her family meals much more interesting and much less like drudgery when she realized that there was something vital in selecting food to protect the health of her family. She said the feeding of a family reminded her of the planning of a house, where plans must be carefully made to provide for all the various uses of the house without waste of material or energy.

The feeding of a family should be such as to build up or to maintain health and vitality in every member. Therefore it must include a plan for the needs of the family in terms of Calories, protein, phosphorus, calcium, and iron, with an estimate of the amount of food required to provide these food substances. The food must be selected with vitamin value, with va-

riety, and with flavor in mind. It should be prepared in a digestible, palatable, and attractive manner.

The Food Needs of the Irving Family

Let us review the conditions in the Irving family
which Mrs. Irving had to consider in planning their
meals. They are as follows:

Mr. Irving, a salesman, was forty-four years of age
and weighed 145 pounds. He had a good appetite
and enjoyed hearty meals. His work varied from light
to heavy.

Mrs. Irving was forty-two years old, weighed 160
pounds, and did her own housework, with the exception of the washing and the heavy cleaning. She ate
heartily, but did not seem to have much endurance.
She was overweight, as her normal weight was 132
pounds.

Grandma Irving, who was sixty-eight years old,
weighed 120 pounds. She helped with the light work
and the mending.

There were Tom, Alice, Clare, and Dick, of school
age, and Jack and Betty, not yet of school age.

Mrs. Irving estimated the food needs of her family
as shown in Table XXXVI.

According to these figures, Mrs. Irving must plan
meals to provide during the course of the day, about
20,000 Calories, 550 grams of protein, between 7 and
8 grams of calcium, from 9 to 10 grams of phosphorus,
and about 0.10 gram of iron. Calculated in shares,
the food requirement of the Irving family was as
shown in Table XXXVII.

TABLE XXXVI. — THE FOOD REQUIREMENTS OF THE IRVING
FAMILY IN CALORIES AND GRAMS

	AGE	WEIGHT	CALO-RIES	PRO-TEIN [2]	CAL-CIUM	PHOS-PHORUS	IRON
	Years	Pounds		Grams	Grams	Grams	Grams
Mr. Irving . .	44	145	3000	73	0.65	1.23	0.015
Mrs. Irving . .	42	160	2800[1]	66[1]	0.59[1]	1.14[1]	0.013[1]
Grandma Irving .	68	120	1650	60	0.52	1.03	0.012
Tom	15	120	4500[4]	90[4]	1.00	1.00	0.015[4]
Alice	14	90	2200	66	1.00	1.00	0.011
Clare	10	65	1900	57	1.00	1.00	0.010
Dick	7	40	1800[3]	54	1.00	1.00	0.009
Jack	3	34	1300	39	1.00	1.00	0.007
Betty	1	20	1000	30	1.00	1.00	0.005
Totals for the day . . .			20,150	535	7.76	9.40	0.097

[1] Food requirements of Mrs. Irving are calculated according to her normal weight which is 132 pounds.

[2] Protein requirements for the children are calculated at the rate of 30 grams per 1000 Calories.

[3] Because Dick is underweight, he needs extra food.

[4] Since it is probable that the requirements for protein and mineral elements do not increase in proportion to energy needs above a 3000 Calorie requirement, Tom's protein and iron are calculated on the basis of 3000 Calories.

Practice brings familiarity. It is obviously impossible for any woman with a family as large as the Irving family to figure out each day the exact amount of food required to furnish the exact amount of these foodstuffs, but Mrs. Irving was wise enough to foresee that it would be well to work out the plans for two or three days. In this way the composition of foods and the effect of each on the total food value of the diet became so familiar to her that she was able to judge whether or not the meals were well-balanced

TABLE XXXVII. — THE FOOD REQUIREMENTS OF THE IRVING
FAMILY IN TERMS OF SHARES

	AGE	WEIGHT	CALO-RIES	PRO-TEIN	CAL-CIUM	PHOS-PHORUS	IRON
	Years	*Pounds*	*Shares*	*Shares*	*Shares*	*Shares*	*Shares*
Mr. Irving . .	44	145	30	29	28	28	30
Mrs. Irving . .	42	160	28	26	26	26	26
Grandma Irving .	68	120	16	24	23	23	24
Tom	15	120	45	36	43	23	30
Alice	14	90	22	26	43	23	22
Clare	10	65	19	23	43	23	20
Dick	7	40	18	22	43	23	18
Jack	3	34	13	16	43	23	14
Betty	1	20	10	12	43	23	10
Totals for the day . . .			201	214	335	215	194

without detailed planning thereafter. Her experiences in her search for Calories, protein, calcium,
phosphorus, iron, and vitamins are given below.

Mrs. Irving's Experiences

Planning the meals for a day. In planning the
meals, milk was Mrs. Irving's first consideration. She
allowed a quart a day each for Betty, Jack, Dick,
Clare, Alice, and Tom, with a pint each for Mr. Irving, grandma, and herself. This made seven and one
half quarts. It seemed like a large amount, but, since
it was so important for health, Mrs. Irving preferred
to economize on something else, if need be. Of the
entire amount of foodstuffs required for the day, this
amount of milk furnished 5070 Calories, 244 grams
of protein, 8.8 grams of calcium, 6.8 grams of phosphorus, and 0.018 gram of iron. Mrs. Irving recorded

her decisions in tables similar to Tables XXXVIII and XXXIX, meanwhile making a mental note that the milk provided all the calcium her family needed so she would not have to plan to get any more of this factor into the diet in other ways.

As iron was another food factor likely to be deficient, Mrs. Irving's next concern was to make the dietary rich in iron. Because whole grain cereals are richer in iron, other mineral elements, and vitamins B and G than are the other more refined cereals, she decided that the whole family must have a whole grain cereal for breakfast. Bananas, sliced and mixed with the cereal, added Calories and other food factors, and served for fresh fruit for the family, with the exceptions of Betty and Jack who had orange juice. Creamed eggs on graham toast was added to the breakfast. Seven hard-cooked eggs, chopped and mixed with three cups of white sauce, made an ample amount. With white bread toast, milk for the children, and coffee for grandma and Mr. and Mrs. Irving, the breakfast plan was complete.

From force of habit, Mrs. Irving allowed four pounds of meat for her family dinner, but, as this seemed to make the protein too high, she reduced the meat to one pound. This amount did not seem very bountiful for seven people (for Jack and Betty would not be allowed to have meat), but, combined with one to two pounds of rice and some left-over vegetables, it made a very attractive dish. The rice was cooked; it was then mixed with the chopped meat and with two cups of chopped carrot and a little onion and green pepper that had been left over from the day before; the loaf was baked in the oven for one half hour. Mrs. Irving had made a similar dish once before when there was a small amount of cooked meat left over from a meal, and Tom had remarked at that time, "My, but that's good, mother! Why haven't we ever had it before?" Mrs. Irving saved some of the cooked rice for Betty; Jack and his grandmother had some of the rice cooked with the meat, but with the meat removed. With the main dish decided upon, Mrs. Irving thought of gingerbread for dessert, because the children were very fond of it, because it contained molasses which would add a little more iron, and because it provided energy and a sweet dish. Each of the children was to have a glass of milk at noon, but Mrs. Irving was undecided about the noon vegetable.

It did not seem advisable to serve both rice and potatoes at the same meal, but potatoes could be served for supper. "They are such an excellent food, according to the books," said Mrs. Irving, "because they are valuable for energy, iron, and other mineral elements, and they have an alkaline reaction." Potatoes are good creamed, escalloped, or baked, but Mrs. Irving decided to cream them for supper so as to use some of the cream sauce on graham toast for Betty and Jack. As she prepared prunes for Betty and Jack each day, it seemed convenient to have prune pudding for the whole family at the evening meal, thereby adding more iron, and supplying in a very harmless form the sweetness all children crave.

But even with dark cereals, eggs, meat, potatoes, and prunes to furnish iron, Mrs. Irving felt that she must make the diet still richer in this very important factor, and, besides, she had not arranged to serve a green leafy vegetable as yet. The family was very fond of asparagus, but that was out of season, and cauliflower was too expensive. Spinach was in season, for she had seen it in the market the previous day; she also remembered how valuable it was for iron and vitamin A. Since the whole family, including Betty, could eat it, spinach was the choice for a vegetable to be served at night with the creamed potatoes. A glass of milk for each child, with tea for the adult members of the family, completed this meal.

Reviewing her success, Mrs. Irving was satisfied that the calcium requirement of her family was more than met by the milk alone; the protein need was taken care of by milk, meat, and eggs, with such additional amounts as were obtained in grain products and potatoes. Vitamin A was surely adequately supplied by whole milk, butter, eggs, and spinach; it seemed safe to depend on the vegetables and whole grain bread and cereals for vitamins B and G. But, as Mrs. Irving compared the food requirement sheet of her family with her meal plans, she discovered that vitamin C was not yet provided for as liberally as she wished. She had three alternatives; namely, to give orange or grapefruit instead of, or in addition to, banana in the morning, but this was rather expensive for a regular practice; or she could serve tomatoes for a vegetable, or prepare a green leafy vegetable in salad. Since the family were to have spinach for supper, it seemed best to have the tomatoes, for she had no gravy to serve with the meat loaf, and stewed tomatoes would help to make good this deficiency; moreover it would provide additional vitamin C with benefit to every member of her family.

The only thing that had to be made specially for the children was a custard for Jack's dinner. With an orange for Betty and Jack, the meals as planned, are shown in Table XXXVIII, with the food values calculated in Table XXXIX.

Although the food values were slightly higher than the estimated amounts, this was an error on the right side of the equation, as the chances were that some of the meat loaf, or the spinach, or the potato would be left to go toward the food value of the following day's meals.

When Mrs. Irving figured up the cost of the food for the day, she could hardly believe her eyes. It was more than a dollar less than she had been in the habit of spending. This seemed unbelievable! She had written down the seven and one half quarts of milk with determination, as she knew that the family needed it, but she had done it in fear and trembling, expecting her food bill to be much higher because of it.

As she was curious to see how the food value of the meals she had been in the habit of preparing compared with this plan, she worked out a typical one, and the results are shown in Table XL.

PROBLEM

85. Prepare the meals carefully planned by Mrs. Irving for her family. Calculate the cost of these meals. Calculate the cost of the day's meals not planned according to food values. Which are cheaper?

Is Appetite a Reliable Guide?

As Mrs. Irving compared the two diets, she saw that her former meals were below requirements in some respects and above in others. The energy was high and the mineral elements were comparatively low. Had the amount of food been only just enough to satisfy the energy needs of the family, the mineral elements would have been sadly deficient. The cost was also high, so that there had been waste of both food and money in trying to get what the system needed. Mrs. Irving realized that in the past her chief idea had been to give her family something to satisfy the appetite. This method had proved to be expensive. Her family also gave evidence to the fact that the food they had been receiving was not such as to give them maximum health and strength for the future; this had become clear to Mrs. Irving because of their marked improvement soon after the new method of feeding was started.

There was too much of a chance for error in working without a plan. Therefore Mrs. Irving concluded that she would not risk the health of her children by using any uncertain methods, but would give careful thought to the planning of the family's meals. Whereupon, she sat down with her paper and pencil to work out some kind of system. She thought of all the facts which were recorded in the books; of the various things she had learned during her brief period of scientific meal-planning; and of the many errors she had made in the past. The results of her deliberations on these points are recorded on page 255.

TABLE XXXVIII. — MRS. IRVING'S MEAL PLAN

	BETTY	JACK	DICK AND CLARE	TOM AND ALICE	MR. AND MRS. IRVING AND GRANDMA IRVING
Breakfast	Oatmeal, top milk. Toast. Milk to drink	Oatmeal, top milk. Buttered toast. Milk	Sliced banana. Oatmeal, thin cream. Creamed egg. Buttered toast. Milk	Sliced banana. Oatmeal, thin cream. Creamed egg. Buttered toast. Milk	Sliced banana. Oatmeal, thin cream.[1] Creamed eggs. Buttered toast.[2] Coffee
9 A.M.	Orange juice	Orange			
Mid-morning luncheon	Graham bread. Milk				
Dinner	Boiled rice with milk. ½ egg, 1 tbsp. spinach. Toast. 1 tbsp. carrot	Rice from meat loaf. Tomatoes, stewed. Spinach. Bread, butter. Milk. Baked custard	Rice-meat loaf. Tomatoes, stewed. Bread, butter. Ginger-bread. Milk	Rice-meat loaf. Tomatoes, stewed. Bread, butter. Ginger-bread. Milk	Rice-meat loaf. Tomatoes, stewed. Bread, butter.[3] Gingerbread. Tea
Supper	Graham bread toast. Cream sauce. Milk. Prune pulp	Graham bread toast. Cream sauce. Prune pulp	Creamed potatoes. Spinach. Bread, butter. Prune pudding. Milk	Creamed potatoes. Spinach. Bread, butter. Prune pudding	Creamed potatoes. Spinach. Bread, butter.[3] Prune pudding. Tea

[1] Mrs. Irving had no cereal.
[2] Grandma Irving ate no toast for breakfast.
[3] Mrs. Irving and Grandma Irving ate no bread for dinner or supper.

TABLE XXXIX. — THE FOOD VALUE OF THE MEALS GIVEN
IN TABLE XXXVIII

FOOD	QUANTITY	CALORIES	PROTEIN	CALCIUM	PHOSPHORUS	IRON
				ESTIMATED DAILY REQUIREMENTS		
		20,150	Grams 535	Grams 7.76	Grams 9.40	Grams 0.097
General supplies						
Milk . . .	7½ qt.	5070	244	8.82	6.79	0.018
Bread:						
white . .	1 lb.	1174	42	0.13	0.41	0.004
graham . .	1 lb.	1180	40	0.24	0.99	0.011
Fat . . .	1 lb.	3491	4	. . .	. . .	. . .
Sugar . . .	6 oz.	680	. . .	. . .	. . .	. . .
Breakfast						
Bananas . .	4(22 oz.)	400	5	0.04	0.12	0.002
Oatmeal . .	12 oz.	1352	57	0.23	1.34	0.013
Oranges . .	2	150	2	0.13	0.06	0.001
Eggs . .	8	560	50	0.25	0.68	0.012
Dinner						
Meat . . .	1 lb.	860	86	0.05	0.93	0.013
Rice . . .	1 lb.	1591	37	0.02	0.43	0.005
Carrots . .	10 oz.	106	3	0.13	0.11	0.001
Tomatoes .	1¾ lbs. (canned)	171	9	0.09	0.19	0.003
Gingerbread .		1460	24	0.44	0.09	0.015
Supper . .						
Potatoes . .	3 lb.	912	24	0.15	0.63	0.014
Flour . . .	2 oz.	200	6	0.01	0.05	0.001
Spinach . .	2 lb.	216	19	0.61	0.62	0.033
Prunes . .	¾ lb.	870	6	0.15	0.30	0.009
Totals for the day .		20,443	658	11.49	13.74	0.155

Calculated according to shares, the above meals
have a food value as follows:

CALORIES	PROTEIN	CALCIUM	PHOSPHORUS	IRON
Shares 204	Shares 300	Shares 490	Shares 350	Shares 290

TABLE XL. — THE FOOD VALUE OF MEALS PLANNED BY MRS. IRVING
WHERE CALCULATIONS HAD NOT BEEN MADE

FOOD	QUANTITY	CALORIES	PROTEIN	CALCIUM	PHOSPHORUS	IRON
		ESTIMATED DAILY REQUIREMENT				
		20,150	Grams 535	Grams 7.76	Grams 9.40	Grams 0.097
General supplies						
Milk . . .	2 qt.	1256	60	2.19	1.68	0.004
Bread, white .	1 lb.	1174	42	0.13	.041	.0004
Butter and fat	1 lb.	3488	5	. . .	. . .	. . .
Sugar . . .	1½ lb.	2721	. . .	. . .	. . .	. . .
Breakfast						
Cream of wheat . .	½ lb.	802	25	0.05	0.28	0.002
Cream (18%)	½ pint	440	6	0.22	0.19	. . .
Eggs . . .	6	447	41	0.20	0.55	0.009
Bananas . .	7	700	9	0.06	0.28	0.005
Luncheon						
Potatoes . .	1½ lb.	456	12	0.07	0.32	0.007
Tomatoes .	3 lb.	309	12	0.16	0.35	0.005
Oil . . .	½ lb.	2041	. . .	. . .	. . .	. . .
Cake . . .	1 lb.	1600	32	0.18	0.56	0.006
Dinner						
Lamb chops .	2 lb.	2850	167	0.10	1.80	0.025
Potatoes . .	2 lb.	608	16	0.10	0.42	0.009
Beets . . .	1 lb.	167	6	0.11	0.14	0.002
Tapioca . .	½ lb.	804	1	0.03	0.20	0.004
Apples . .	½ lb.	107	1	0.01	0.02	0.001
Totals		19,970	435	3.61	7.20	0.083
"Extras" eaten during the day						
Candy . .	¾ lb.	1413	8	. . .	. . .	. . .
Cake . . .	1 lb.	1600	32	0.18	0.56	0.006
Apples .	2 lb.	428	4	0.04	0.08	0.004
Meals and "extras"		23,411	479	3.83	7.84	0.093

A Practical Method for the Planning of Well-Balanced Meals

The conclusions which Mrs. Irving gathered from her accurate plans are as follows:

In order that one may be sure of getting all the materials needed by the body for growth, repair, regulating, and energy, the diet should contain:

1. Milk

    1 quart for everyone when possible

    1 quart for all children under six years old, for each adolescent boy and girl, and for each malnourished or underweight child

    At least 1 pint for all those who do not have a quart

2. Grain Products   *Amount depending on the activity of the person*

For children under two years of age	1–3 oz. a day
For children from two to five	2–5 oz. a day
For children from five to twelve	5–9 oz. a day
For those over twelve years .	9–16 oz. a day

3. Meat or its equivalent   *No meat needed and*

For children under five . . .	no meat to be given
For children from five to ten . .	not more than 1–2 oz.
For children from ten to fourteen .	not more than 2–3 oz.
All people over fourteen years . . .	not more than 2–6 oz.

   (a) Eggs   For children under five years . . 3–5 a week

          For children over five years, 3–5 a week if possible

          (Eggs may be substituted for meat when desired.)

   (b) Peas   These may be used in place of a part or all of the

      Beans   meat as a source of protein, but there should

      Cheese   be plenty of milk with the beans and peas.

4. Vegetables

    Serve at least two vegetables every day, one of which should usually be potatoes, with a leafy vegetable three or four times a week or as much oftener as possible. Other vegetables may be given in addition to those named above or alternating with the green leafy vegetables.

5. Fruit

Serve fruit at least once every day. Citrus fruit should be given three or four times a week to everyone, unless there are plenty of raw, green leaves and tomatoes in the diet daily.

Dried and other fresh fruit may be given in addition to, or alternating with, citrus fruit.

6. Sweets

Have a sweet dessert once or twice a day if desired, but serve very little if any clear sugar, as on cereals, or in the form of candy.

7. Fats

Use two to three ounces of fat (purchased as such) for each person over five, the amount depending on the age.

If a meal contains the right foods in the right proportions, and if each person eats enough to maintain a normal weight, has good color in his cheeks, a sparkle of health in his eye, and good resistance, one need feel no further concern about the quantity eaten.

COMBINATIONS FOR MEALS

The manner of combining foods is not so essential as the foods themselves. A meal may be a several-course dinner, or it may consist of but one dish. It may be bread and milk. Whole wheat bread is to be preferred, but if white bread is served there should be something with it to increase the iron. A meal may consist of soup alone, but if so there should be plenty of cereals and vegetables in the soup to provide energy, as there is danger of deficiency in energy where one depends too much upon a liquid diet.

Here are a few suggestions that it is well to keep in mind when planning meals:

There should be only one heavy protein dish in any meal.

There should always be plenty of energy at each meal.

Clear soups are expensive. Their chief function is to stimulate a "lazy" appetite. They should not be given to children as a regular diet. The capacity of the stomach of a child is limited, and there is danger that he will not get all the energy needed, if too much soup is eaten.

A thin soup and cocoa make a poor combination for the reason just stated. A thin soup and a fruit salad make a combination deficient in energy and protein. With a soup it is far better to serve a cereal or custard dessert containing concentrated food value.

A cream soup, a heavy meat dish, and an egg or milk dessert make a poor combination.

A cream soup with a hearty dessert is sufficient for a meal, provided they supplement one another in food value.

Meals Should Be Served Attractively

Other important considerations, especially for school children, are the regularity with which meals are eaten, and the manner in which the food is served. Food that should appeal to the appetite might be served in such a way as to make it seem quite unappetizing. Milk served in a plain white cup, with some toast on a clean white plate, and a neatly cut piece of butter at the side — all placed on a white cover (it may be very cheap white muslin, or it may be clean oilcloth, or it may be clean white paper) — may be much more appetizing than a costly luncheon served unattractively.

Dishes and table as well as food should be kept clean, not only for sanitary reasons, but also for the psychological effect it has on the eye, which, in turn, is reflected in the nerves to the stomach. It may not be possible to have expensive dishes, silver, and linen, but it is always possible to keep those one has clean and shining.

PROBLEMS

86. Plan a series of one-dish meals where the one dish contains the desired amount of energy-producing foods, protein, mineral elements, and vitamins for a family of four. Let the various members of the class prepare these dishes, compare, and serve them in an attractive manner.

87. Plan, prepare, and serve a day's meals for the family of some member of the class, applying the suggestions and rules given throughout the chapter.

THE SCORE CARD, A MEANS OF JUDGING THE RELATIVE MERITS OF A MEAL

There are various factors to be considered in judging the relative merits of two or more meals. If each student in the class were to prepare a meal as a test of her ability to plan, purchase, and prepare the meals for a family, and if the teacher were to give each student a mark, she would doubtless have some difficulty, because there would be favorable and unfavorable points about each meal. Therefore, the following score card has been devised, whereby the various points may be marked according to a score:

SCORE CARD

I. Planning the meal . . . . 75 points
- Energy . . . . 30 points
  - Consider ages, weights, and occupations.
- Protein . . . . 15 points
  - Is protein suitable in kind and amount?
- Mineral elements . . . . 15 points
  - Calcium . . . . 5 points
  - Phosphorus . . . 5 points
  - Iron . . . . . 5 points
- Vitamins . . . . . . 15 points
  - Vitamin A . . . 5 points
  - Vitamins B and G . 5 points
  - Vitamin C . . . 5 points

II. Selection and preparation . . . . 15 points
- Is the food cooked in a digestible manner and in such a way as to retain vitamins and minerals? 5 points
- Are combinations of foods pleasing to the eye, and is the food attractively served? . . . 5 points
- Is the food sufficiently bulky? . 5 points

III. Purchasing of the food . . . . . 10 points
- Is the food fresh and of good quality?
- Is there a good return for the money spent?
- Is the food adapted to the income of the family?

PROBLEM

88. With the aid of the score card shown above, score the meals planned in Problems 85 and 87.

QUESTIONS

1. What is your reaction to the statement, "Appetite is a reliable guide"?

2. What ought to prevent the planning of meals from becoming a bore to a mother?

3. What should be the first step in the planning of meals?

4. Discuss the practical method suggested by Mrs. Irving for planning well-balanced meals.

5. Discuss the manner suggested for the combining of foods in a meal.

6. How may you judge the relative value of the various points which must be considered in a meal? Discuss the division of the credits and points in the suggested plan.

7. Completion test:
     A quart of milk will furnish —— grams of calcium.
     A pound of spinach contains —— gram of iron.
     A pound of lean beef contains —— grams of protein.
     Citrus fruits and tomatoes are the best sources of ——.

REFERENCES

For students and teachers:

BAILEY, N. B. *Meal Planning and Table Service.* The Manual Arts Press.

DOWD, M. T. and JAMESON, J. J. *Food and Its Preparation,* Chapter XXII. John Wiley & Sons (1925).

FARMER, F. M. *Boston Cooking School Cook Book,* revised edition. Little, Brown, and Company (1921).

GUNN, L. M. *Table Service and Decoration.* J. B. Lippincott Co. (1928).

HARRIS, J. W. and LACEY, E. V. *Everyday Foods.* Houghton Mifflin Company (1927).

LORD, ISABEL E. *Everybody's Cook Book.* Henry Holt Co. (1924).

ROSE, MARY S. *Feeding the Family,* third edition, Chapters XIII and XIV. The Macmillan Company (1929).

CHAPTER XIV

THE MARKET ORDER AND METHODS OF BUYING

ALICE DOES THE MARKETING

During the summer vacation, Alice was to be initiated into the secrets of wise buying and a family market order. She was to plan the meals, buy the food for the family for a certain amount each week, make sure that the food requirements of the family were satisfied, and hand to her mother at the end of the week an itemized bill of expenses. The only condition imposed was the use of at least seven and one half quarts of milk a day.

As Mrs. Irving looked back over the past eighteen years, during which she had been responsible for the feeding of a family, her method of planning meals and of marketing seemed to her like a bit of hit-or-miss drudgery. There was an absence of that feeling of satisfaction which should be the reward of work well done. Many a pleasant afternoon out had been spoiled by the annoying query all the way home as to what she was going to have for dinner, and whether there were any of this or that in the house. Then, with the one idea of getting something easily prepared she would start for market and go from one place to another, only to hear the dealer say, "All out, madam." Or else she would find the stock picked over and a poor quality left, or the price more than she could afford to pay — and, not knowing what else to do, she would buy the higher priced food and try to economize on something that was more essential than the thing purchased. This last-minute planning had caused Mrs. Irving so much anxiety that now, as she spent more time in planning ahead, she experienced much satisfaction, and her family's meals were better.

PLANNING AHEAD

As Alice, like most novices in buying, thought it would be too much work to plan in advance the groceries she would need for the week, her mother decided that a little experience in planning both by the day and by the week might be valuable for purposes of comparison. During the first week Alice planned the meals each day with a great deal of care, calculated the exact quantity of each food needed, and bought just the right amount, sometimes going to market two or three times during the day. Frequently the calculating of food values was not completed until evening, after the meals were eaten. Oftentimes she would find that the family had had too little iron or calcium, or more protein or energy than they needed. The protein was most perplexing, for it was always too high, and yet she did not see how it could be reduced. At the end of the sixth day the money for the week gave out, and she had to borrow from her mother.

LEAKS IN BUYING

When her mother went over the accounts at the end of the week, Alice was $3.00 in debt. The first item catching her attention was three pounds of meat on each of the first four days of the week, at from 40 to 60 cents per pound. In response to her mother's suggestion that meat not only had increased the protein unduly but also was expensive, Alice replied that these purchases had been made at the first of the week, before she had realized how quickly the money was going to give out. "That is just the reason," said her mother, "why it is well to work on a weekly basis, so that you will be sure to have as much money for food on the last day of the week as on the first."

The rest of the itemized bill showed that Alice had bought cheese at five different times during the week, each time getting only ten cents' worth. To calculate the food value of the cheese, however, it had been necessary to weigh it at home, where she found she had received about three and one third ounces each time for her ten cents. Her mother asked her how much it was a pound, but it had not occurred to her to inquire. Upon inquiry she found the cheese to be 40 cents a pound, although she had been paying for it at the rate of 50 cents a pound. Then her mother told her that it is always well to ask how much things are a pound, and to ask for a certain number of ounces or pounds, rather than to tell how much one has to spend. The ten cents wasted on the cheese would have bought two fine oranges for Betty. Betty had had to go without fresh fruit for several days because the funds were running low. The list in Table XLI gives an itemized account of other similar leaks that had caused Alice to go into debt.

Mutliplying $2.95 by 52 gives $153.40. Then a

leakage of $2.95 a week means a total loss for the year
of over $150, which might have been spent for more

TABLE XLI. — LEAKS IN ALICE'S GROCERY ORDER WHERE FOOD
VALUE DISAPPEARED

		WHAT SHE PAID	WHAT SHE SHOULD HAVE PAID	LOSS
		Cents	*Cents*	*Cents*
Butter . .	One pound of butter at 55¢ a pound, purchased in 4 different lots. Each purchase cost 15¢ . . .	60	55	5
Cheese. .	One pound of cheese, purchased in five 10¢ lots, with cheese at 40¢ per pound	50	40	10
Eggs . . .	Six eggs, purchased singly at 6¢ each, when eggs were 66¢ a dozen	36	33	3
Macaroni	One package (10 ounces) for 15¢, making macaroni 24¢ a pound, when in bulk it was 12¢ a pound . .	15	8	7
Meat . . .	Six to eight pounds more than was necessary but, as something else would have been substituted for part of this, there might have been a saving of perhaps $2.40 . . .			240
Potatoes.	One and one half pecks potatoes, purchased in three-pound lots at 4¢ a pound, when potatoes were 45¢ a peck	96	68	28
Prunes. .	Two pounds of prunes at 19¢ a pound, purchased in half pound lots at 10¢ each lot	40	38	2
	Total waste			$2.95

food, or for other items of expense, or which might have been saved against a rainy day. Had there not been a standing order for seven and one half quarts of milk daily, Alice might have bought her milk a pint at a time, and would thus have wasted still more money. Planning at short range is an extravagant use of time, of money, and, if food value is sacrificed thereby, of health.

METHODS OF BUYING

After the experience just related, Alice was quite ready to follow her mother's advice: first, to calculate the food values needed for the whole week; second, to plan the meals in a general way so as to make the market order for the week. She decided to hand this order to the grocer during the week — for instance, on Wednesday, when the grocer was not so busy as on Saturday morning. She planned to purchase sugar, potatoes, cereals, coffee, tea, canned goods, butter, and eggs for the week, adding salt, baking powder, and spices when they were needed. She also decided that she could purchase fruit and meat twice a week and vegetables every other day. This meant that she would not have to go to market each morning, and could often plan her meals from what she had in the refrigerator. Her mother agreed that it would be impossible for her to make detailed plans until she knew what she would have in the way of left-overs.

By the time Alice had purchased and calculated the food values of a few weekly grocery orders, she could judge approximately the amount of each of the various types of food required to provide the proper kind of meals for the family. She soon became quite expert in planning and buying. It seemed to her that the more limited the amount to spend, the more necessary was a weekly plan, and the more the following points needed to be emphasized:

1. Make an inventory of food on hand before making the market list.

2. Buy in quantities as large as money, storage facilities, and keeping qualities will permit.

3. Form the habit of reading the labels on canned goods, and know what sizes, brands, or grades give the best value for the price paid. Household sizes of canned goods are numbered ½, 1, 2, and 2½. Size 2 holds enough for four people. Size 2½ holds enough for six people, and is more economical for a large family. Canned fruits and vegetables are usually more expensive than fresh fruits and vegetables.

4. Ask the price of food; then ask for a definite weight or measure rather than for so many cents' worth. Compute the amount you should receive for the price you pay. Buy as many articles by weight as you can.

5. Select a market and become a regular customer. In this way you will receive better service, and the clerks will become familiar with the grade of goods you wish to purchase.

6. Check your order when it comes from the store, and put the food away yourself if you can; this will help you to remember what you have on hand.

7. Among the grain products, oatmeal and whole wheat flour have the highest food value, because of the high mineral content, especially iron. Ready-to-eat cereals are relatively expensive.

8. Plan one quart of milk for each child and one pint for each adult. Evaporated and skimmed milk may be used to good advantage in cooking.

9. At all times it should be kept in mind that fat and sugar contain practically no mineral elements, and that the mineral elements in the diet will be deficient if these foods are depended upon to furnish too large a percentage of the energy.

10. Molasses is unlike sugar in that it is rich in both iron and calcium and is a good laxative.

11. Butter substitutes may be used for all persons over five years of age and for children under five years where the maximum amount of fresh milk and some green leafy vegetables are given every day.

12. It is poor economy to buy butter, a quarter of a pound at a time. If you have no ice in summer, put the butter in a covered bowl or jar, and arrange to keep it as suggested for milk on page 181.

13. Very small prunes or very large prunes are relatively expensive (the latter because they command high prices, the former because they are so largely stone). Those numbering 40 to 60 to the pound are most economical.

14. The more one has to economize, the less should be the amount of meat used. The cheaper cuts of meat not only cost less but contain more food value per pound. A fireless cooker will save fuel.

15. If one can afford the space in her pantry or food closet, a shelf which contains enough canned goods to supply one or two meals will be found most convenient. This may be called an emergency shelf.

PROBLEMS

89. Make a list of the foods you think could be ordered in weekly quantities, or in larger quantities when there is room for storage.

90. Estimate the number of pounds of each of the supplies listed in Problem 89 which in your judgment would be needed by the Irving family, for a week. Figure these estimates in terms of your own family and make out the weekly market order.

91. How many pounds of meat a week would you allow the Irving family? Which will be the most economical type to order: roasts, steaks, chops, fish, poultry, or tougher cuts of meat? What kind of meat should be purchased for meat pies, casserole dishes, hash, and one-dish meals? Suggest ways of preparing meat so that a little will go a long way in the flavoring of the dish.

92. Make a list of foods that might be purchased at a good delicatessen store. Calculate and compare the delicatessen store price and the price when cooked at home. Are time and fuel to be considered in food economy?

93. Compare the price of prunes by the 10-pound box in the fall with the price of prunes later in the winter. How does the

size of the prune affect the price?   Do large prunes contain any more nourishment than small prunes?

94. When fresh fruit is high, how will you manage to supply the family with its equivalent?   What members of the family must have some fresh fruit each week?   Compare the cost of dried-apple sauce with fresh-apple sauce.   Compare the cost of stewed dried peaches with that of canned peaches. Do oranges go farther in marmalade than when fresh?   Do you think that jellies and jams and canned fruit could take the place of fresh fruit for the adults?

95. When and how could you use dried milk?   How much does dried milk cost per quart?   When and how could you use oleomargarine or nut butter?   If oleomargarine or nut butter is used instead of butter, how much money is saved?

96. Compare the cost of cereals bought in bulk with that of cereals bought in a package.   Compare the cost of cereals bought ready to serve with that of cereals that must be cooked.   Are time and fuel the only things to consider here?

97. Compare the prices of food purchased in stores where no telephone orders are taken and no deliveries made with the prices of food purchased in stores where such accommodations are given.   Does it pay to take the time to do your own marketing?

A Short Way to a Well-planned Diet

As Alice struggled with her problem during the summer months, she often wondered how people who have no one to advise them make "both ends meet."   She wondered particularly about those who know nothing of food values and those who have gone directly from the shop or factory into homes of their own.   The more she thought about it, the closer seemed the relationship between the wistful, hungry look in the thin, pale faces of so many underweight children and the family market order. In her short experience she had found it quite possible to spend plenty of money for food without getting plenty of food value.

Others have thought about this same thing. Sherman, of Columbia University, New York City, who has studied food chemistry very thoroughly, thought about the problem so much that he felt it ought to be possible to devise some way whereby families, especially the children, would be getting all the food value needed even when it was not possible to calculate the value of the diet. He felt that the suggestions might be made so simple that, even though the one who did the buying had no knowledge of the relative value of different foods, she might be guided aright.

He was instrumental in having made and supervised the study of the diet and market orders in 100 families where there were growing children. As a result of this study he concluded that the diet would be suited to the needs of the family if the following suggestions were used in making out the market order:

Of the money spent for food:

1. As much or more should be spent for milk as for meat.
2. As much or more should be spent for vegetables and fruits combined as for meat; or
3. No more should be spent for meat than for milk, or for vegetables and fruits combined.

Another suggestion which has been found useful in purchasing food for a large family with limited means, is to divide the money to be spent for food into fifths, as follows:

One fifth, more or less, for vegetables and fruits

One fifth, or more, for milk and cheese

One fifth, or more, for bread and cereals, including flour

One fifth, or less, for fats, sugars, other groceries, and food adjuncts

One fifth, or less, for meat, fish, and eggs

Rearranging the family market order according to these suggestions without increasing the amount spent for food has since been tried n hundreds of families where there were malnourished children with whom the doctors said nothing was wrong except their food. The quick response in improved condition, in the color of the cheeks, and in the sparkle of the eye is enough to assure us that it is a very satisfactory method.

In the majority of families, the amount of money spent for food is sufficient to keep children well fed if it is spent wisely. In one family in which there were eight children, three of whom were suspected of having tuberculosis and all of whom were underweight, the mother spent five dollars less a week after her diet and market order were adjusted to conform to the suggestions given above. It is almost unbelieveable that for the first time in months the children began to gain in weight on the new diet. The changes made were "more milk and vegetables and less meat." This is only one of many instances where the children have improved wonderfully, and where the amount of money spent for food is considerably less with a properly planned diet.

It is well known that the more one has to economize, the larger should be the amount of grain products used to provide sufficient energy. In the studies referred to above, the low-cost diets were not furnishing all the energy needed by active children unless the mother was spending about one fourth or one fifth of all the money spent for food in buying the more economical grain products. This, then, gives us another very helpful suggestion to be used when we must provide a large amount of nourishment for a very limited amount of money, and with the grain products it is essential to have generous amounts of milk and vegetables, especially those kinds represented in Charts XXVII and XXVIII.

Charts XXV, XXVI, XXVII, and XXVIII represent the amount of nourishment the family already referred to were receiving in return for the money they were spending for the various types of food, and the relative value of foods within each type.

**Some Foods Supply Building Material
More Economically than Others**

The length of the line opposite the food given below indicates the
return in food value for the money spent

Milk or cheese

Bread, cereals
macaroni, or rice

Vegetables

Meat, eggs
or nuts

Courtesy of the N.Y.A.I.C.P.

Chart XXV

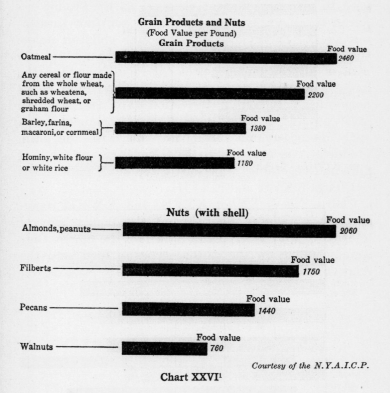

Grain Products and Nuts
(Food Value per Pound)
Grain Products

Oatmeal ——————— Food value 2460

Any cereal or flour made from the whole wheat, such as wheatena, shredded wheat, or graham flour — Food value 2200

Barley, farina, macaroni, or cornmeal — Food value 1380

Hominy, white flour or white rice — Food value 1180

Nuts (with shell)

Almonds, peanuts——— Food value 2060

Filberts ————— Food value 1750

Pecans ————— Food value 1440

Walnuts ———— Food value 760

Courtesy of the N.Y.A.I.C.P.

Chart XXVI[1]

[1] The numbers given under "Food Value," in Charts XXVI, XXVII, and XXVIII, are the "composite valuations," or "score values," computed as described by L. H. Gillett in publications of the N.Y.A.I.C.P.

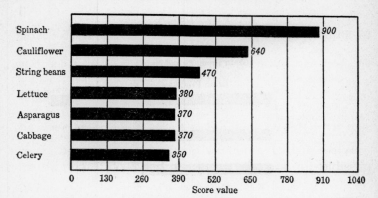

Chart XXVII. — Green and leafy vegetables — A comparison of the score value per pound [1]

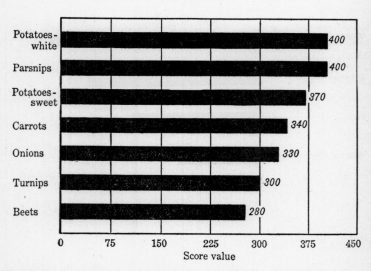

Chart XXVIII.— Roots and tubers — a comparison of the score value per pound [1]

[1] See footnote on page 273.

PROBLEMS

98. Plan the meals for a week for the family of some member of the class.

99. Work out the grocery, dairy, butcher, and fish orders for these meals, and calculate the cost. How does it compare with the amount ordinarily spent by families (of a corresponding size) of the various members of the class?

Keep a Record of Food Purchased

With such a guide as Sherman has devised, it is possible for anyone to adjust her food expenditures

Weekly Record for Food

Is the food well-planned for the health of the children?
(Put down amount, kind, and cost)

Date............

Bread, Cereals, Cakes, Flour, Rice, Macaroni	Cost	Milk, Cheese, Cream	Cost	Meat, Fish, Eggs	Cost	Vegetables, Fruits	Cost	Other Groceries, such as Butter, Sugar, Tea, Coffee	Cost
	$		$		$		$		$
Totals									

Courtesy of the N.Y.A.I.C.P.

so as to get a good return in food value for the money
spent.   But to know whether or not one is getting
fully adequate amounts of nutriment, it will be necessary to keep some kind of record of the food purchased.
After a few weeks of accurate record keeping, one should
be able to estimate the divisions of her food expenses
without this detailed account.

The sheet on page 275 has been found useful in helping the mothers of these same underweight children
to study and to plan the proper spending of the food
money.   It has helped many mothers to keep their
children from becoming underweight.

Some such record as this will enable one to compare the totals spent for each type of food and to see
whether the expenditures have been wise or not.

COMPUTING THE CALORIES

If we compute the Calories furnished by the various
foods purchased, we have another check on our food
expenditures.   Dr. Mary S. Rose, of Columbia University, New York City, has suggested[1] the following
approximate division of total Calories:

	More expensive diet	*Less expensive diet*
Cereal foods	$\frac{1}{6}$ of Calories	$\frac{1}{3}$ of Calories
Milk	$\frac{1}{4}$ of Calories	$\frac{1}{4}$ of Calories
Vegetables and fruits . .	$\frac{1}{5}$ of Calories	$\frac{1}{7}$ of Calories
Fats	$\frac{1}{8}$ of Calories	$\frac{1}{14}$ of Calories
Sugars	$\frac{1}{8}$ of Calories	$\frac{1}{14}$ of Calories
Meat, fish, eggs, cheese . .	$\frac{1}{8}$ of Calories	$\frac{1}{8}$ of Calories

[1] From "Wise Buying," by M. S. Rose, in *Modern Priscilla*, 1923

PROBLEMS

100. From your weekly record of food, judge its "balance of food values," according to the relation of the amount spent for different types of food.

101. During the Christmas or the Easter vacation, assume the entire responsibility for the ordering of the food in your home. For purposes of discussion, bring your results to class recorded on a form similar to the one on page 275?

QUESTIONS[1]

1. What are the laws of your state which control retail food selling?

2. What are your city ordinances which affect the handling of food?

3. What are the laws in your state regarding weights and measures?

4. What do you consider are your responsibilities with regard to the enforcement of these laws?

5. In what ways can the consumer coöperate with the retail seller to lower the cost of selling and thus to bring down the price of food?

REFERENCES

For students:

HARRIS, J. W. and LACEY, E. V. *Everyday Foods*, Chapter XXVII, pages 160 to 168; Chapter XXIV, pages 232 to 240; Unit Six, pages 354 and 355. Houghton Mifflin Company (1927).

MONROE, D. and STRATTON, L. M. *Food Buying and Our Markets*, Chapters I, II, XI, XII, XV, and XVI. Barrows (1928).

Farmers' Bulletins No. 1044, 1144, and 1196. U. S. Department of Agriculture.

[1] Determine the answers to the questions above by outside inquiry and investigation.

For teachers:

ANDREWS, B. R.   *Economics of the Household,* Chapter IX.   The
Macmillan Company (1923).

DONHAM, S. A.   *Marketing and Household Manual,* pages 3 to 79.
Little, Brown and Company (1918).

NYSTROM, P. H.   *Economics of Retailing,* second edition, Chapter
XVI.   The Ronald Press Company (1919).

SHERMAN, H. C.   *Food Products,* second edition.   The Macmillan Company (1924).

INDEX

Absorption of food, 65–66
Acids, 92–93
Activity, influence on energy requirement, 47–49
Adenoids, 6
Adolescence, weight increase during, 150
Adults
  Calorie requirement for adults, 50
  energy requirement, average-sized man, 48–49
  food, 219–241
  food requirement of, 130, 134
Age, influence on food requirement, 55–56
Alkalis. See Bases
Alligator pears. See Avocado
Almonds, 38, 74, 79, 97, 100, 103, 125, 139
Aluminum, 89
Amino acids, 81–83
Antineuritic vitamin. See Vitamin B
Antiophthalmic vitamin. See Vitamin A
Antiscorbutic vitamin. See Vitamin C
Appetite
  as guide in selection of food, 251
  during adolescence, 150
Apples, 32, 33, 69, 74, 77, 79, 96, 97, 99, 100, 102, 103, 122, 139, 212
Apricots, 32, 33, 74, 79, 97, 100, 103, 122, 139
Arsenic, 89
Asparagus, 34, 74, 79, 97, 100, 103, 120, 139
Atwater, W. O., 47
Avocado, 33, 122, 139

Babies
  best food, 167
  bottle-fed, formula for, 172
  bottles, care of, 181–182
  diet, 165–184
    adding new foods, 179
    cereals, 170
    first year, 178
    foods other than milk, 167
    fourteen to eighteen months of age, 193–194
    fruit, 190
    hours for feeding, 173
    number of feedings, 171–172
    orange juice, 169
    regularity essential, 176
    second year, 186–195
    supplementary, for first year, 174–175
    tomato juice, 169
    vegetables, 189
    weaning, 173
  health habits, 182–184
  health requirements, 165
  sunlight, effect on, 182–184
  weaning, 173
  weight increase, 4, 6, 166–167
  See also Children
Bacon, 37, 74, 79, 97, 100, 103, 124, 139
Bacon fat, 35
Baking soda, 118
Bananas, 33, 74, 79, 97, 100, 103, 122, 139
Barley, 30, 31, 74, 123
Basal energy requirement, 47
Bases (alkalis), 92–93
Beans
  baked, 34
  canned, 34

Beans— *continued*
  dried, 78, 131
  kidney, 120, 139
  Lima, 34, 74, 79, 97, 100, 120, 139
  navy, 139
  string, 34, 74, 79, 96, 97, 99, 100,
    102, 103, 120, 139
  white, 34, 74, 97, 100, 120
Beef, 37, 77, 79, 96, 97, 99, 100, 102,
    103, 125, 139
Beef drippings, 35
Beef liver, 125, 141
Beets, 34, 74, 79, 97, 100, 103, 121,
    139
Benedict, F. G., 47
Beri-beri, 112
Blackberries, 33, 74, 79, 97, 100, 103,
    122, 139
Blueberries, 74, 79, 97, 103, 122, 139
Bluefish, 37, 139
Bologna sausage, 37, 125
Bomb calorimeter, description of,
    27–28
Bottles, feeding
  care of, 181–182
Box luncheon, 162
Boys
  food requirement, 130
  height
    average, 16
    increase, 5
    over five years, 14–15
  weight
    annual gain, 16
    average, 16
    increase, 4
    over five years, 14–15
  See also Children
Brazil nuts, 38
Bread, 74, 78, 92, 174–175, 191, 203,
    207, 227
  brown, 31, 79, 97, 100, 103, 123,
    139
  graham, 31, 79, 97, 100, 103, 123,
    139
  hot, 228–229
  rye, 31, 79, 97, 100, 103, 123, 139
  white, 31, 79, 97, 100, 103, 123,
    139
    amount of each food factor in,
      138

Bread— *continued*
  whole wheat, 31, 79, 97, 100, 103,
    123, 139, 207
Breakfast, 152, 156, 223
Brussels sprouts, 34, 79, 97, 100, 103,
    121, 140
Buckwheat flour, 79, 97, 100, 103,
    123, 141
Butter, 35, 69, 74, 77, 79, 96, 97, 99,
    100, 102, 103, 124, 140, 191–
    192, 211
Buttermilk, 35, 74, 79, 97, 100, 103,
    125, 140
Butternuts, 38
Buying. *See* Marketing

Cabbage, 34, 74, 79, 97, 100, 103,
    121, 140, 231
Calcium, 89, 93, 135, 137, 138, 153–
    155
  daily requirement, 95, 153, 154
  deficiency of, 154, 198
  functions in, 93–95
  grams in 100-Calorie portions of
    common foods, 96, 97, 120–
    121, 122, 123, 124, 125–126
  influence on growth, 94–95
  safety allowance, 95
  sources, 96–98
Calories, 153–154
  adults, requirement, 50
  computing, 276
  energy requirement, measured in,
    45–46
  explanation of, 27–28
  number required for each pound
    of body weight during grow-
    ing period, 55
  100-Calorie portions, 28–39
    basis of share system, 133–134
    grams of calcium in common
      foods, 96, 97, 120–121, 122,
      123, 124, 125–126
    grams of carbohydrate in com-
      mon foods, 74
    grams of fat in common foods,
      74, 75
    grams of iron in common foods,
      102, 103, 120–121, 122, 123,
      124, 125–126

Calories— *continued*
grams of phosphorus in common foods, 99, 100, 120–121,
122, 123, 124, 125–126
grams of protein in common
foods, 77, 79, 120–121, 122,
123, 124, 125–126
share value of, 139–143
weight and measure of 100-
Calorie portions
chocolate, 39
dairy products, 35–36
eggs, 35–36
fats, 35–36
fish, 37–38
fruits, 32–33
grain products, 30–32
meat, 37–38
nuts, 38
sugar, 39
vegetables, 34–35
Calorimeter
bomb, description of, 27–28
respiration, description of, 46
Candy, 234
Cantaloupes, 74, 79, 97, 100, 103,
122, 140
Carbohydrates, 67–69
comparison of amounts in common foods, 69
composition of, 62
grams in 100-Calorie portions of
common foods, 74
sources, 68–69
Carrots, 34, 74, 79, 97, 100, 103, 121,
140
Cauliflower, 34, 74, 79, 97, 100, 103,
121, 140
Celery, 34, 74, 79, 97, 100, 103, 121,
140
Cellulose, 72
Cereal products, 123
Cereals, 78, 92, 174–175, 203–207
cooking, 205–206
fried, 228–229
teaching children to like, 204–205
value of, in diet, 170, 191, 203,
227
Chard, 74, 79, 97, 100, 103, 121, 140
Cheese, 69, 77, 78, 79, 92, 96, 97, 99,
100, 102, 103, 125, 131, 226

Cheese— *continued*
American, 35, 74, 125, 140
cottage, 35, 226
cream, 35, 226
Swiss, 35
Cherries, 74, 79, 97, 100, 103, 122,
140
candied, 39
stoned, 33
Chestnuts, 38, 74, 79, 97, 100, 103,
125, 140
Chicken, 139
broiled, 37
canned, 37, 125
Children
diet
one year old, 178
fourteen to eighteen months of
age, 193–194
during second year, 186–195
during third year, 200
during fourth year, 214
during fifth year, 215
from two to five years of age,
197–216
supplementary for first year,
174–175
energy requirement, 52–54
food, 52–54, 219–241
allowances, 53
forbidden foods in, 213
height
over five years, 10–11, 14–15
under five years, 9
weight
over five years, 10–11, 14–15
under five years, 9
See also Babies
Chlorine, 89
Chocolate, 39, 79, 97, 100, 103, 124,
125, 140
weight and measure of 100-Calorie
portions, 39
Citron, 32
Clams, 37, 79, 97, 100, 125, 140
Clothing, relation to food requirement, 58–59
Cocoa, 39, 79, 97, 100, 103, 124, 125,
140, 202
Coconut, 38, 74, 79, 97, 100, 103,
125, 140

Cod-liver oil, 35, 120, 168, 174–175, 236
  source of vitamin A, 210
  source of vitamin D, 210
Cod steak, 140
Coffee, 202, 220
Conjunctivitis, 110
Constipation
  causes of, 237–238
  curative measures, 237–238
  effects of, 237
  exercise, value of, 237
  foods recommended to overcome, 238
  water, value of, 237
Copper, 89
Corn, 34, 74, 79, 92, 97, 100, 103, 121, 140, 231
Corn syrup, 39
Cornflakes, 31
Cornmeal, 31, 74, 79, 97, 100, 103, 123, 140
Cornstarch, 31
Cottonseed meal, 97, 100, 123
Cottonseed oil, 35
Cow's milk, as substitute for mother's milk, 170, 173
Crackers
  graham, 31
  saltine, 31
  soda, 31, 79, 97, 100, 103, 123, 140
Cranberries, 33, 79, 92, 97, 100, 103, 122, 140
Cream, 100, 103
  thick, 36, 74, 79, 124, 140
  thin, 36, 74, 79, 97, 124, 140
  whipped, 36
Crisco, 36, 124
Cucumbers, 34, 74, 79, 97, 100, 103, 121, 140, 231
Currants, 32, 33, 74, 79, 97, 100, 103, 122, 140
Cystine, 81

Dairy products, 69, 77, 96, 99, 102
  weight and measure of 100-Calorie portions, 35–36
Dandelions, 34, 74, 79, 97, 100, 103, 121, 140
Dates, 32, 74, 79, 97, 100, 103, 122, 140

Dextrin, 71
Diet
  adults, 220–226
  anti-constipation, 237–238
  calculating by shares, 133–134
  children
    one year old, 178
    fourteen to eighteen months of age, 193–194
    during second year, 186–195
    during third year, 200
    during fourth year, 214
    during fifth year, 215
    from two to five years of age, 197–216
  fat in, 76
  milk as basis of, 199–202
  planning by shares, 138
  skin eruption, relation to, 154–155
  well-planned, 269–272
Digestion, 63–65
Digestive tract, 64
Dinner, 153, 156, 224
Drugs, 237
Duck, 140

Eby, M. F., 137
Economy in buying, 265–268
Egg white, 36, 125, 141, 168, 210
Egg yolk, 36, 125, 141, 168, 174–175, 210
Eggplant, 34, 74, 79, 97, 100, 103, 121, 140
Eggs, 36, 74, 77, 78, 79, 92, 96, 97, 99, 100, 102, 103, 125, 131, 140, 210, 233
  weight and measure of 100-Calorie portions, 35–36
Endive, 34, 121, 141
Energy
  amount varies with conditions, 46–51
  basal requirement, 47
  food, relation of, 1–3
  food as source, 2, 191
  replacement, 44
  reserve supply, 43–44, 59, 65
  sources, 37, 40–41, 67–68, 70, 71, 73
    fats, 40–41, 67–68, 73, 235
    food, 2, 191

Energy—*continued*
    oils, 40–41
    starches, 67–68, 71
    sugar, 67–68, 70
  value of different foods, 40–41
Energy requirement
  adults, 48–49, 50–51
  after middle age, 55–56
  baby, first year, 171
  basal, 47
  children, 52–54
  clothing, influence of, 58–59
  difference in men and women, 50–51
  first year of life, 171
  growth, influence of, 52–54
  high-school age, 154–155
  measured in Calories, 45–46
  mental work, influence of, 57–58
  muscular activity, influence of, 44, 47–49
  variations, 50
  varies with conditions, 46–51
Excretion of waste, 66, 189
Exercise
  relation to growth, 7–8
  value in constipation, 237

Family
  feeding the, 147–163
  planning meals for, 129, 221–224, 243–259, 262
  See also Irving family
Farina, 32, 74, 79, 97, 100, 103, 123, 141
Fats, 67–68, 69, 72–76, 77, 78, 96, 99, 102, 124, 131, 211–212, 256
  amount in diet, 76
  comparison of amounts in common foods, 75
  composition of, 62, 72–73
  energy value of, 40–41, 67–68, 73, 235
  grams in 100-Calorie portions of common foods, 74
  source of energy, 40–41, 67–68, 73, 235
  sources, 73–75
  weight and measure of 100-Calorie portions, 35–36

Feeding schedules for
  babies, 171–173
  child during first year, 174–177
  child during second year, 186–195
Figs, 32, 33, 74, 79, 97, 100, 103, 122, 141
Filberts, 38, 74, 125, 141
Fireless cooker, 206
Fish, 74, 79, 92, 97, 100, 103, 125, 131, 233
  weight and measure of 100-Calorie portions, 37–38
Flour, 74
  buckwheat, 79, 97, 100, 103, 123, 141
  graham, 32, 79, 97, 100, 103, 123, 141
  rye, 79, 97, 100, 103, 123, 141
  wheat (entire), 32, 69, 79, 97, 100, 102, 103, 123, 141
  white, 32, 79, 96, 97, 99, 100, 102, 103, 123, 141
Fluorine, 89
Food
  absorption of, 65–66
  acid-base influence, 92–93
  acid-forming, 92
  adolescence
    large amount required during, 150
  adult requirement, 130, 134
  base-forming, 92
  buying, 261–276
    leaks in, 262–265
    methods of, 265–268
  calcium in, 96–98
  children, 53
    one year old, 178
    fourteen to eighteen months of age, 193–194
    during second year, 186–195
    during third year, 200
    during fourth year, 214
    during fifth year, 215
    from two to five years of age, 197–216
    supplementary, for first year, 174–175
  children's food compared with that of adults, 219–241
  children's requirements, 130

Food—*continued*
  composition of, 61–85
  dependence on, 1–23
  digestion, 63–65
  economy, relative, of various types, 272
  energy value of, 26–41
  factor in good nutrition, 1, 6, 67
  forbidden, for children one to five, 213
  fried, harmful for children, 228–229
  fuel value of, 27–28
  groups, 62
  growth, relation to, 1–3, 52–54
  interrelationships, 66–67
  market order, 261–276
  100-Calorie portions. *See* Calories — 100-Calorie portions; Calories — Weight and measure of 100-Calorie portions
  planning of, 129, 221–224, 243–259, 262
  record of weekly purchases, 275–276
  requirement. *See* Energy requirement
  selection of, 26–27, 129–143
    according to food groups, 131–132
  methods, 130
    shares, 133–134
    value in terms of grams, 132–133
  share value of 100-Calorie portions, 139–143
  source of energy, 2, 191
  value. *See* Food values
  value in shares, 136–138
  vitamin value of common foods, 120–126
  weighing, 28
Food requirement. *See* Energy requirement
Food values, comparison of, 153–155, 273
Fowl, 79, 97, 100, 103, 125, 233
Frankfurters, 37
Fresh air, relation to growth, 7
Fruit, 32, 33, 69, 74, 77, 78, 92, 96, 99, 102, 122, 131, 190, 207, 232–233, 256

Fruit—*continued*
  weight and measure of 100-Calorie portions, 32–33
Fuel value of food, 27–28

Gelatin, 37, 82, 125
  Irish moss, 104
Ginger, crystallized, 39
Girls
  food requirement of, 130
  height
    average, 12
    increase, 5
    over five years, 10–11
  weight
    annual gain, 13
    average, 12
    increase, 4
    over five years, 10–11
    See also Children
Gliadin, 83
Glycogen, sources, 71
Goiter, 104
Goose, 141
Graham flour, 32, 79, 97, 100, 103, 123, 141
Grain products, 69, 77, 96, 99, 102, 131, 203, 227, 255, 273
  weight and measure of 100-Calorie portions, 30–32
  See also Cereals
Grape juice, 33, 141
Grapefruit, 79, 97, 100, 103, 122, 141
Grapenuts, 32
Grapes, 33, 69, 74, 79, 97, 100, 103, 122, 141
Growth
  calcium, influence of, 94–95
  curves showing influence of tryptophane and lysine, 81
  effect of milk on, 188–189
  effect of vitamin A, 109
  effect of vitamin B, 113
  effect of vitamin G, 113
  factors
    exercise, 7–8
    fresh air, 7
    milk, 188–189
    posture, 8
    sleep, 6–7

Growth, factors—*continued*
    sunlight, 7, 182–184
    vitamin A, 108–109
    vitamin B, 113
    vitamin G, 113
    water, 8
  food, relation of, 1–3, 52–54
  food requirement, relation of, 52–54
  mineral elements, relation of, 89–92
  periods of rapid, 3–6
  proteins, relation of, 80–81
  rate of, 2–3
  salt mixture, effect on, 90, 91

Haddock, 141
Halibut steak, 37, 141
Ham, 37, 125, 141
Hazelnuts, 79, 97, 100, 103, 125
Health
  appearance not indication of, 197
  factors, 1–3
    exercise, 7–8
    food, 6
    fresh air, 7
    posture, 8, 151
    regularity, 176
    sleep, 6–7
    sunlight, 7
    vegetables, 230–232
    water, 8
    weight, 22
  food, relation of, 1–3
  habits. *See* Health habits
  physical defects, effects of, 6
  score card, 23
Health habits, 23, 216, 236
  babies, 182–184
Heat
  effect on vitamin A, 112
  effect on vitamin C, 117
Height
  boys
    average, 16
    increase per year, 5
    over five years, 14–15
  children
    under five, 9
  girls
    average, 12

Height, girls—*continued*
    increase per year, 5
    over five years, 10–11
Herring, 141
Hickory nuts, 38
Histidine, 81
Hominy, 32, 74, 79, 97, 100, 103, 123, 141
Honey, 39, 74, 79, 97, 100, 103, 124, 141
Huckleberries, 33
Hundred-Calorie portions. *See* Calories — 100-Calorie portions; Calories — weight and measure of 100-Calorie portions

Iodine, 89, 93
  functions, 104
  sources, 104
Iron, 89, 93, 135, 137, 138, 153–155
  adults' daily requirement, 101
  children's daily requirement, 101
  foods valuable for, 101–102
  functions, 101
  grams in 100-Calorie portions of common foods, 102, 103, 120–121, 122, 123, 124, 125–126
  safety allowance, 101
  sources, 101–102
Irving family
  feeding the, 147–163
  food needs of, 244, 245, 246
  meal plan, 252
  planning meals, 221–224, 243–259, 262
    for one day, 246–250
  three substantial meals, 155–156
  Betty (one year old), 147, 166–167
    feeding schedule, 176–177
    food, 165–184
    food value of diet, 192
    meals during second year, 188–189
    number of meals a day, 195
    schedule for second year, 187–188
    weaning, 173
  Jack (three years old), 147
    bread, 207
    butter, 211–212

Irving family, Jack—*continued*
   cereals, 204–205
   cod-liver oil, 210–211
   diet, 197–199
   eggs, 210
   fruit, 207
   health habits, 216
   meat, 211
   milk, 199–202
   oatmeal, 204–205
   teeth, 207
   vegetables, 208–209
  Dick (seven years old), 148, 219
  Clare (ten years old), 148, 219–220
  Alice (fourteen years old), 148, 155
   fatigue, 150
   food requirement, 154
   loss of weight, 150
   luncheon, 156–158, 159
   marketing, 261–268
   meals, 152–155
  Tom (fifteen years old), 149
   doctor's advice, 150
   food requirement, 154
   lack of strength, 150
   luncheon, 156–158, 159
   meals, 152–155
  Mr. Irving, 220
  Mrs. Irving, 220
   reducing, 238–240
  Grandma Irving, 220

Jam, 124, 233
Jelly, 233

Kale, 34, 121, 141
Kidney, 125, 141
Kohl-rabi, 74, 79, 97, 100, 103, 121, 141

Lactose, 69–70
Lamb, 79, 97, 100, 103
  breast, 141
  chops, 37, 125, 141
  leg, 37, 125, 141
  roast, 37
Lard, 74, 97
Legumes, 78

Lemons, 33, 74, 79, 97, 100, 103, 122, 141
Lentils, 34, 74, 78, 79, 97, 100, 103, 121, 141
Lettuce, 34, 74, 79, 97, 100, 103, 121, 141
Liver, 37, 125, 126, 141
Lobster, canned, 37, 126
Lunch counter, school, 159
Luncheon, 152–153, 156, 223–224
  box, 162
  high-school students, 152–155
  home-cooked, 157–158
  mid-afternoon, 156
Lusk, Graham, 47, 51
Lysine, 81, 83

Macaroni, 32, 74, 79, 92, 97, 100, 103, 123, 141
Mackerel, 37, 141
Magnesium, 89
Malted milk, 36
Manganese, 89
Maple sugar, 39
Maple syrup, 39, 74, 79, 97, 100, 103, 124, 142
Marketing, 261–276
  leaks in buying, 262–265
  methods of buying, 265–268
Mayonnaise dressing, 36
McCollum, E. V., 108
Meals
  breakfast, 223
  children
   one year old, 178
   fourteen to eighteen months of age, 193–194
   during second year, 186–195
   during third year, 200
   during fourth year, 214
   during fifth year, 215
   from two to five years of age, 197–216
  combinations for, 256–257
  dinner, 224
  food value of, 253, 254
  for Alice Irving, 152–155
  for Tom Irving, 152–155
  luncheon, 223–224
  plan for the family, 252–253

Meals—*continued*
planning
ahead, 262
for a family, 221–224, 243–259
for one day, 246–250
method, 129, 255–256
score card, 258–259
serving of, 257–258
three substantial, 155–158
typical, of high-school students, 152–155
value of, 152–153
Meat, 69, 74, 77, 78, 92, 96, 99, 102, 125, 131, 191, 211, 233, 255
weight and measure of 100-Calorie portions, 37–38
Mendel, L. B., 198
Mental work, relation to food requirement, 57–58
Mid-afternoon luncheon, 156
Middle age
energy requirement after, 55–56
food requirement modified after, 56
Milk, 69, 74, 78, 92, 97, 102, 131, 188–189, 202, 255
as source of vitamin A, 111
basis of diet, 199–202
buttermilk, 35, 74, 79, 97, 100, 103, 125
clean milk, importance of, 179–180
condensed, 36, 74, 79, 97, 100, 103, 126, 142
cow's, 170, 173
malted, 36
modified. *See* Modified milk
mother's milk. *See* Mother's milk
necessity for all, 224–226
powdered, 36
skimmed, 36, 74, 79, 97, 100, 103, 126, 142
top, 36
whole, 74, 77, 79, 96, 97, 99, 100, 103, 126, 142
Milk sugar. *See* Lactose
Mineral elements, 88–104
composition of, 63
deficiency of, 90–91
definition, 88–89
functions of, 89–92
growth, relation to, 89–92
importance of, 89–92

Modified milk, 170
suggested formula for, 172
Molasses, 39, 74, 79, 97, 100, 103, 124, 142, 212
Mother's milk, 165, 167, 168, 173
best substitute for, 170
Muscular activity, 44, 47–50
Mushrooms, 34, 121, 142
Muskmelon, 33, 142
Mustard greens, 142
Mutton, 37, 79, 97, 100, 103, 126, 142

Nipples, care of, 181–182
Nutrition, food, relation of, 1, 6, 67
Nuts, 74, 78, 125, 235, 273
weight and measure of 100-Calorie portions, 38

Oatmeal, 69, 74, 77, 79, 96, 99, 100, 102, 103, 123, 204
Oats, rolled, 32, 142
Oils, 74
energy value of, 40–41
sources, 73–75
Okra, 34, 121
Oleomargarine, 36
Olive oil, 36
Olives, green, 33, 74, 79, 97, 100, 103, 122, 142
One-hundred Calorie portions. *See* Calories — 100-Calorie portions; Calories — weight and measure of 100-hundred Calorie portions
Onions, 34, 74, 79, 97, 100, 103, 121, 142
Orange juice, 33, 122, 142, 169, 174–175
Oranges, 33, 74, 79, 96, 97, 99, 100, 103, 122, 142, 212
Overweight condition, 238–240
effect of, 68
Oysters, 37, 71, 79, 97, 126, 142

Parsnips, 34, 74, 79, 97, 100, 103, 121, 142
Peaches, 33, 74, 79, 97, 100, 103, 122, 142
Peanut butter, 38, 235

Peanuts, 38, 74, 79, 97, 100, 103, 126, 142
Pears, 33, 74, 79, 97, 100, 103, 122, 142
Peas, 74, 79, 97, 100, 103, 121
 canned, 34
 dried, 78, 131, 142
 fresh, 34, 142
 split, 34, 121
Pecans, 38, 74, 79, 97, 100, 103, 126, 142
Pellagra, 113
Peppers, green, 35, 74, 79, 97, 100, 103, 121, 142
Phosphorus, 89, 93, 135, 137, 138, 153–155
 functions of, 93–94, 98
 grams in 100-Calorie portions of common foods, 99, 100, 120–121, 122, 123, 124, 125–126
 safety allowance, 98–99
 sources, 99–101
Physical defects, effect of, 6
Pigeon, 142
Pine nuts, 38
Pineapple, 74, 79, 97, 100, 103, 122
 canned, 33
 fresh, 33, 142
Plums, 33, 74, 79, 92, 97, 100, 103, 122, 142
Polyneuritis, 112
Pork, 37, 74, 79, 97, 100, 103, 126, 142
Posture
 relation to growth, 8
 standards, 151
Potassium, 89
Potato chips, 35
Potatoes, 69, 77, 78, 79, 96, 97, 99, 102
 sweet, 35, 74, 100, 103, 121, 142
 white, 35, 74, 100, 102, 103, 121, 142
  amount of each food factor in, 137
  share value of, 136
Proline, 81
Protein, 135, 137, 138, 153–155
 amount required daily, 83–85
 children's requirement, 84
 complete, 80–81
 composition of, 62

Protein—continued
 functions of, 78–80
 grams in 100-Calorie portions of common foods, 77, 79, 120–121, 122, 123, 124, 125–126
 incomplete, 80–81
 milk, 82
 relative value of, 80–81
 relative value of common foods for, 78
 sources, 77–78
Prunes, 33, 74, 79, 92, 97, 103, 122, 142
Pumpkins, 74, 79, 97, 100, 103, 121, 142

Quail, 142

Radishes, 35, 74, 79, 97, 100, 103, 121, 142
Raisins, 33, 74, 79, 97, 100, 102, 103, 122, 142, 207
Raspberries, 33, 74, 79, 97, 100, 103, 122, 143
Relative value of foods, 40–41, 75, 77, 78, 272, 273, 274
Respiration calorimeter, description of, 46
Rhubarb, 33, 74, 79, 97, 100, 103, 121, 143
Rice, 32, 74, 77, 78, 79, 92, 97, 100
 brown, 103, 123, 143
 puffed, 32
 white, 100, 103, 112, 123, 143
Rickets, 93, 118, 168
Roots, 274
Rose, Dr. Mary Swartz, 133–134, 276
Rutabagas, 143
Rye flour, 79, 97, 100, 103, 123, 141

Safety zone (weight), 19–21
Salmon
 canned, 38
 fresh, 143
Salt, 104
Sardines, 38, 126, 143
Sausage, 37
Scales, 28
Scallops, 38, 71, 126
Schedules for the feeding of children. See Feeding schedules

School children. *See* Children
School lunch counter, 159
School luncheons, 159–160
Scurvy, 116
Sea weed, 104
Shad, 143
Shares
    calculating diet by, 133–134
    man's requirement, 135
    number required, 135–136
    planning diet by, 138
    value of foods in, 136
Sherman, H. C., 95, 101, 270, 275
Shredded wheat, 32, 74, 79, 100, 103, 123, 143
Shrimps
    canned, 126
    raw, 38
Silicon, 89
Skin eruptions, relation to diet, 154–155
Sleep
    hours required, 6–7
    relation to growth, 6–7
Smelts, 143
Sodium, 89
Spinach, 35, 74, 79, 97, 100, 103, 121, 143
Squab, 143
Squash, 35, 70, 74, 79, 97, 100, 103, 121, 143
Starch, sources, 71
Strawberries, 33, 74, 79, 97, 100, 103, 122, 143
String beans. *See* Beans, string
Succotash, 35
Suet, 36
Sugar, 69–70, 74, 78, 97, 124, 131, 191, 212–213, 234
    brown, 39
    granulated, 39
    loaf, 39
    powdered, 39
    sources, 70
    weight and measure of 100-Calorie portions, 39
Sulphur, 89
Sun baths. *See* Sunlight
Sunlight
    effect on babies, 182–184
    relation to growth, 7, 182–184
    source of vitamin D, 119

Sunshine. *See* Sunlight
Sweets, 212–213, 234, 256

Tapioca, 32, 79, 97, 100, 103, 123, 143
Tea, 202
Teeth
    carious, 6, 63, 93
    effect of vitamin C on, 115–116
Thyroid gland, effect of iodine on, 104
Tigerstedt, R., 51
Tomato juice, 169, 174–175
Tomatoes, 69, 74, 79, 97, 100, 103, 121
    canned, 35, 143
    fresh, 35
Tonsils, 6
Triscuit, 32
Tryptophane, 81
Tubers, 274
Tuna fish, 38, 126, 143
Turkey, 37, 143
Turnips, 35, 74, 79, 100, 103, 121, 143
    tops, 143
Tryosine, 81

Underweight condition, 240–241

Veal, 37, 79, 97, 100, 126, 143
    liver, 37, 126
Vegetables, 69, 77, 92, 96, 99, 102, 117, 120–121, 131, 174–175, 189, 229–232, 255, 274
    serving of, 208
    value of, 208
    weight and measure of 100-Calorie portions, 34–35
Vitamin A, 138, 211
    amount in 100-Calorie portions of common foods, 120–121, 122, 123, 124, 125–126
    deficiency, results of, 108–111, 154
    effect of heat on, 112
    effect on growth, 109
    importance of, 108
    safety allowance, 111
    sources, 111, 168, 211
        cod-liver oil, 210
Vitamin B, 138, 191
    amount in 100-Calorie portions of common foods, 120–121, 122, 123, 124, 125–126

Vitamin—*continued*
  deficiency, results of, 113, 154, 169
  effect of water on, 114
  effect on growth, 113
  functions, 112–113
  importance of, 112–113
  safety allowance, 114
  sources, 113–114
Vitamin C, 138
  amount in 100-Calorie portions of
      common foods, 120–121, 122,
      123, 124, 125–126
  deficiency, results of, 115, 116,
      168, 169
  effect of alkali on, 117
  effect of heat on, 117
  effect of water on, 117
  functions, 115–116
  importance of, 115–116
  safety allowance, 117
  sources, 116–117
Vitamin D
  deficiency, results of, 118, 119,
      167–168
  functions, 118
  sources, 118–119, 168
      cod-liver oil, 210–211
  sunlight, 119
Vitamin E, 120
Vitamin G, 138, 191
  amount in 100-Calorie portions of
      common foods, 120–121, 122,
      123, 124, 125–126
  deficiency, results of, 113, 154, 169
  effect of water on, 114
  effect on growth, 113
  safety allowance, 114
  sources, 113–114
Vitamins
  discovery, 107
  functions, 107–108
Von Norden, 56

Walnuts, 38, 74, 79, 97, 100, 103,
    126, 143
Waste, excretion, 66, 189
Water
  composition of, 63
  effect on vitamin B, 114
  effect on vitamin C, 117
  effect on vitamin G, 114

Water—*continued*
  relation to growth, 8
  value in constipation, 237
Watercress, 121
Watermelon, 33, 74, 79, 97, 100, 103,
    122, 143
Weaning a baby, 173
Weight
  adolescence, 150
  average-weight line, 19
  babies
    increase in first year, 4
    increase in second year, 4
    increase in third year, 6
  boys
    annual gain, 16
    average, 16
    increase per year, 4
    over five years of age, 14–15
  charts, 17
    average-weight line, 19
    safety zone, 19–21
  children
    over five years of age, 10–11,
        14–15
    under five years of age, 9
  gaining, 240–241
  girls
    annual gain, 13
    average, 12
    increase per year, 4
    over five years of age, 10–11
  health factor, 22
  increase during adolescence, 150
  physical fitness, index of, 9
  reducing, 238–240
  safety zone, 19–21
Weight charts
  average-weight line, 19
  preparation of, 17–18
  safety zone, 19–21
Wheat
  puffed, 32
  shredded, 32
  See also Cereals; Grain Products

Xerophthalmia, 110

Zein, 81, 83
Zinc, 89
Zwieback, 32, 207